THE FOUR
LONDONS OF
WILLIAM HOGARTH

THE FOUR
LONDONS OF
WILLIAM HOGARTH

BY ERICK BERRY

Illustrated with
engravings of Hogarth's works

DAVID McKAY COMPANY, INC.
New York
1964

THE FOUR LONDONS OF WILLIAM HOGARTH

COPYRIGHT © 1964 BY
Allena Champlin Best

LIBRARY OF CONGRESS CATALOG CARD NUMBER: 64–12927
MANUFACTURED IN THE UNITED STATES OF AMERICA

FOR
Dorothea Cramer
and
Ida May Cohen, most patient of librarians.

Contents

Illustrations

Between pages 110 and 111

Author's Note

To us, of the twentieth century, there is something hauntingly familiar in the eighteenth century depicted by William Hogarth. The intervening century, with its worthy but prim and smug Victorianism, begins to appear as a freak of history, like Prohibition; an irrelevancy which somehow slipped into our true line of descent. In the seventeen hundreds we are back with our bold bad ancestors again. We may not approve of them, but we know just how they feel.

There are a hundred parallels between the twentieth and the eighteenth centuries. The voluble and opinionated orators in the coffeehouses, who successively held the air from six in the morning until after midnight, are akin to the radio announcers and commentators of today. They offered no commercials to their audiences, but plain and singing invitations to buy were deafeningly furnished by street vendors. A morbid interest in crime and criminals was as amply catered for by printed dying confessions, broadsheets and songs as it is today in newspaper headlines and whodunits. The evil influence upon the young of *The Beggar's Opera* was deplored as that of Grade B movies and TV shows are today. Hogarth's Series, especially *Industry and Idleness* and the *Four Stages of Cruelty* seem like the ancestors of our own comic books, and were aimed at the same class of reader.

My attention was called to William Hogarth some years ago, when no very recent book about him had been published. While I was at work on the research two books appeared and seemed to fill the gap. So for a time I dropped the project. But the man himself kept nagging at me. I strongly disagreed with so much that had been written about him; largely because I felt that it interpreted him as a writer and not as an artist. Hogarth indeed created very unusual pictorial stories, but his approach to life was that of a painter; and it was as a painter, with an artist's characteristic motives and attitude, that I felt he should be viewed if he were to be fully understood.

To me it did not seem that Hogarth had a cryptic and bewildering personality. There is no question but that he was torn between two aims; one was his passion for depicting London as he saw it; the other was his ambition to produce grandiose pictures after the manner of his greatly admired friend Sir James Thornhill. But this duality of aim is a commonplace among artists in all periods. The commercial artist of today may dream of creating noble murals or being hung in the Royal or some other prestigious Academy. This does not mean that he has a split personality; for there is scarcely a creative human who, while earning his bread and butter, does not aim at something beyond his reach. And so it was with William Hogarth.

Also I could not agree with a current view on Hogarth's home life. From his charming portrait of his wife, Jane does not appear to be the tall, statuesque masterful creature which is suggested as half of the comic-looking couple whose other member was a dumpy ineffectual William Hogarth. In his day Hogarth's height of five feet was little below the average, and to have been a foot taller would have qualified him as a freak or a Grenadier Guardsman. David Garrick, almost the same stature as his friend, had inches sufficient to play heroic roles upon the contemporary stage.

According to her picture Jane had sloping shoulders, which were considered beautiful in her day and were scarcely amazonian. Her complexion was fresh, her hands and arms slender and small-boned. She would have fitted neatly into one of those almost child-sized gowns of her period, which we note with surprise in our museums.

Nor could I see that facts warranted the impression of Richard Hogarth—William's father—as a pathetic failure. In his autobiography, written half a century later, William seems to have thought him so; but that was in comparison with his own remarkably successful career. If Richard was a gentle scholar unable to make headway in crude commercial London, who paid William's heavy apprenticeship fees in the Guild of Silversmiths, one of the richest in London? Who set Hogarth's sisters up in their millinery establishment, in a day when goods could not be obtained on consignment and commercial loans were not available? There is no suggestion that the money came from outside the family, or from William himself.

The facts give quite a different character to Richard Hogarth. They show a simple north countryman coming venturously to the metropolis, to carve out a living with such tools as Greek and Latin. He had no powerful city Guild or noble patron to protect or support him; but by private teaching, and translating and proofreading for printers he not only supported his family in middle-class comfort but established them in their own businesses. Life was easier for a professional—though not much—in William's lifetime. For his father, this was a remarkable feat.

Another point frequently overlooked by biographers is the quite remarkably happy home life which supported the artist throughout his whole career. In a day when the keeping of mistresses was the norm for all who could afford it, and seduction of servant girls a polite accomplishment, Billy and his Jane remained a mutually devoted couple. This is emphasized rather than made doubtful by the venomous attacks on Jane by the critics of Hogarth's painting of Sigismunda. She was wholly irrelevant to the issue of whether the aging artist could or could not surpass the work of the Italianate school, but the critics knew the tender spot in which to thrust their rankling barbs.

Almost the strongest motive in William Hogarth's life was his great love for children. His paintings of them are among his most charming work. Childless—which must have been a lasting regret to both Jane and himself —he spread the warmth of his affection over the waifs and strays of London. When that remarkable philanthropist, Captain Coram, was on the point of realizing the ideal for which he had struggled so long, William Hogarth devoted every possible effort to the creation of the Foundling Hospital, and became its first Governor. Children grown too old for the Hospital found a warm welcome in his home. Two of these were staying in his Chiswick house at the time of his death.

I have made no attempt to deal with every one of Hogarth's many engravings. Some of the smaller but not less interesting ones were issued as part of subscription tickets, the holder to cut off the numbered part of the ticket and retain the engraving as a bonus. All of the genre pictures have been dealt with, so far as possible in what I believe to be the mood and purpose in which they were conceived. But William Hogarth was so hardworking and prolific that it would take a far longer tale than this to deal with all his lesser works.

E. B.

THE FOUR LONDONS
OF WILLIAM HOGARTH

AULD HOGGARD'S
LONDON

1: *The Never-never Land*

IN THE low-beamed, smoky Crook and Shuttle alehouse the soft buzz of talk in the broad Westmorland speech was at its height. Auld Hoggard emptied his pint pot and set the pewter down with a rap on the oak trestle table. The potboy scurried to refill it. Auld Hoggard could bide a while, till the evening's talk had stilled, before he launched his main story of the evening. Let them wait and gather thirst for it. Besides, Richard might be along soon, and if he broke into the midst of the telling 'twould be all the better. It wouldn't do for an elder to seem to seek out a younger brother.

The dim, firelit alehouse smelled of sheep, as it had every right to, being in the small town of Kendal which earned its living from sheep and wool. On the bench around the crowded room a score or more of gaunt, lean men hunched over their crooks, a ha'penny leather cup of ale in each right hand, a tangle-coated dog beneath each seat. For Westmorland county meant sheep, sheep on every fell and moorland, from Solway Firth to Morecambe Bay, from the Pennines to the sea; shorn wool in every staple house, in every carding house and on every distaff. In this year of 1696 wool was the wealth of England, as it had been for more than four hundred years.

The shepherds with their unshorn locks and heavy woolen cloaks, their patient muddy dogs, meant sheep, reeked of sheep and even looked a mite like sheep. For though the weaver's shuttle limned on the creaking sign outside was an invitation to Kendal's more prosperous weavers, few of them patronized the place, turning up their long Flemish noses at the smell. While the shepherds, almost as unvocal as their flocks, couldn't abide the weavers' tongues, which clacked as ceaselessly as their busy heddles.

Auld Hoggard, like all true Westmorlanders, had tended the flocks when he was a lad, held sheep for the shearer, washed and sorted fleeces. Here he was known as the Bard of Kendal, but if he were ever crowned 'twould be with no wreath of laurel, but with a twist of noyly wool. When he had inherited the small family property he became a yeoman farmer and, though he hadn't stuck to his books like brother Richard, he was better schooled than most. He could tally and keep accounts. He could take a happening and make a story of it, or a homely song to set folks chuckling. The Christmastide mummers had acted two plays of his, and Parson had laughed as loud as any.

Auld Hoggard emptied his tankard, but set it down

softly, without the rap that demanded a refill. His fellow farmers ceased their low-toned talk of weather and pasture and coming prices, and turned to listen to him.

"Round where I live at Kirkby Thore there's talk that Hugo Bruges the weaver is wedding Maggie Burnside, who's fallen heir to the farm."

"Plied his shuttle well," agreed another yeoman, with a trace of envy. "Don't seem hardly fitting a long-nosed Fleming should have the handling of one of the best flocks in the Vale of Brampton."

"Heard tell he's minded to call in my brother Richard who teaches Greek and Latin and suchlike." Auld Hoggard glanced around the room, letting a puzzled silence breed a mute question. Then supplied the answer.

"The Burnside dogs know naught but plain English. Hugo will need Richard to teach them to bark in Flemish." He drove his point home with a lusty "Haw! Haw! Ho! Ho!"

"Ohoho! Hoho!" One man, then another echoed the Bard's gusty laughter, for 'twas a jest after their own hearts. A weaver might be born and bred in Westmorland, like his father and grandfather, but was still a foreigner, a Fleming. He should keep to his loom, and let those who knew sheep handle sheep.

A man stooped to pat his dog. "Tha's ignorant as mysen, Blackie," he informed it. "Tha don't speak aught but Westmorland, nor tha sheep neither!"

The Bard rapped his empty tankard on the arm of the settle, and threw back his head in song.

> "The weaver knows his shuttle
> The shepherd knows his dog."

The tankard pounded out the refrain.

> "*Clack, clack, clack,*
> *Bow, wow, wow.*
>
> "If shepherd throws a shuttle
> And weaver sends a dog"

Lustily the farmers joined in the chorus

> "*Clack, clack, clack,*
> *Bow, wow, wow!*"

Before the next verse Auld Hoggard paused, his little deep-set eyes a-twinkle.

> "The sheep don't heed the shuttle
> Nor cloth get wove by dog.
> "*Clack, clack, clack,*
> *Bow, wow, wow!*"

Taciturn shepherds joined in the chorus, and puzzled dogs rose to their feet to add their barking to the din.

> "So 'tis weaver to his shuttle
> And shepherd. . . ."

Whatever the sage advice was to be, turned into a bellow of "Richard!" For the outer door had opened and a man entered, stooping beneath the low lintel, and shaking the rain from his cloak. Lean as a shepherd he was, and not so warmly clad, stooping a little beneath the weight of book learning. But, to judge by the warmth of the welcome given him, success—or some might account it failure—had not set him apart, and he seemed to know even the dogs by name.

He laid a hand on his brother's shoulder, and at his nod the potboy brought two more ales.

"So tha's really venturing to London, lad?" Auld Hoggard asked.

"Lunnon! Tha's never!" The surprise of farmers and shepherds made amends for the lost last verse.

"Aye. A man must eat, and his woman, too." Richard nodded cheerful confirmation. "There's no trade for me here but tallying bales and adding figures. For what does a weaver's, or even a wool merchant's, son need of Greek or Latin?"

"Or a farmer?" Auld Hoggard agreed. "'Twas waste of a good man when Dad took 'ee from the sheep and sent 'ee to the Abbey for more learning than tha'll ever need." Then feeling that he had been unduly sentimental for an older brother, he remembered that one of Richard's pupils had pined away, from overstraining his brain it was believed. "But seeing tha's killing off all tha pupils, tha'd best take to tha heels."

"And one pupil more or less won't be missed in London." Richard grinned.

"Lunnon," opined a shepherd who had never set foot beyond the next valley, "Lunnon's a wonnerfu' town."

"There's more folk in London alone than in all Westmorland—or so 'tis said," a farmer contributed doubtfully.

"True enough. One man in ten of all England lives there." Richard spoke with the authority of learning.

But that was going too far beyond what the imagination could compass. Yeomen and shepherds can count and measure as well as anyone, and know that there's a natural limit set to all things. Why, if you took one man in ten—and of course their women and children—of Westmorland alone and set him down in a city, there'd be neither elbow nor breathing room. Besides being as foolish as trying to drive all Westmorland livestock into one valley. Heads wagged in doubt.

Richard might well be right, but for the sake of the Hoggard good name the Auld One preferred to pass his statement off as a joke. "With so many folk in London there'll be no space for crops nor grazing. Times will come when they'll need to fa' back on eating each other." But the aleroom company still looked solemn. So he pointed his jest. "But they'll no eat thee, Richard, without tha covers tha bones."

Richard laughed with the others. "True enough. But there's no broth in books."

Now that he had talked the company round, the Bard could afford to give his own views. "We're none so ignorant here we don't know about London town. There's the river, bigger than any hereabouts. There's the Tower where the Queen keeps her jewels safe from the Londoners. There's Parliament, where people are paid to do naught but sit and talk. There's a bridge, so old and so strong that there's houses stretching right across from bank to bank. And streams of wagons and coaches along every street by night and by day, so there's no space to cross, but folks born on one side are bound to live on that side until they die. And from three miles out you can smell the stench of London, worse than a thousand sheep . . ."

"There's no smell to sheep," protested a shepherd, and raised an unintended laugh.

"For every honest man, Richard," warned Auld Hoggard, "Tha'll meet a dozen highwaymen and cutpurses. But there's playhouses, too," he added wistfully, "with trained actors to talk the words, and as many as a hundred candles to light the stage. I'd like fine to see that."

"There's tha chance, Auld One. Go with tha brother Richard," another farmer broke in. "Carry tha plays to Lunnon, to the pretty playmistresses."

"Then who'd be left to tend the Hoggard farm?" Auld Hoggard spoke sharply, perhaps in self-reproach for his dreams. "And who's to tell I'd ever find the town? Oh, there's a London all right, we all know that. But none such place as they tell of. That stands to reason. When I drew nigh 'twould shrink to no more than a two-three Kendals. 'Twill serve me best to keep my farm and my London too.

Richard buried his surprise in his tankard, and drained the last of the ale. He laid down his leather tokens in payment, and rose.

"You'll eat and lie with us tonight, brother, or Ann will be angered with me. 'Tis too far for you to ride home in this black storm." Auld Hoggard would think nothing of the fifteen miles to Kirkby Thore, but would need the double excuse to stay and discuss the London venture. Richard made his farewells to the rest of the company, and wrapped his wet cloak around more closely.

The helm wind from the snowy Pennines on the east was biting, though the rain had lessened. Windows were shuttered against it, leaving the narrow streets in darkness, the town of Kendal seemingly uninhabited. But late as it was the clack-clack of battens and the thump of treadles sounded from nearly every house. Often Richard had envied the industrious weavers. Sometimes he had almost envied the Auld One the security of the family farm. It was too small to divide, and by custom had been left to the firstborn. Not till tonight had Richard suspected that Auld Hoggard, that sturdy prosperous yeoman, had ever looked beyond his stone fences or dreamed of aught outside his native Westmorland. Certainly not London.

Auld Hoggard's "So tha's really venturing to London?" had been as great a surprise. Richard had told no one, not even his wife or elder brother, for there was nothing to tell but a wish. But the challenge had turned the wish into a purpose. And that purpose was already becoming a plan.

Dirk van Dissel, an old pupil, was to take his father's woolen cloth to York, and perhaps on to Bruges by ship. For the overland journey he would take packhorses and two men for protection against footpads and highwaymen. Ann would be safe in such company. At York she and Richard could take the regular wagon to London. They would not be strangers in that big city, for they could settle in the Flemish quarter, among friends and relatives of the Kendal weavers whom they knew so well.

Auld Hoggard had given his approval in advance. But what would Ann think? Ann Gibbon, Westmorland born, who, disdaining all neighborly advice, had married a man who was neither farmer nor weaver, neither fish nor fowl. She had a will of her own. Would she approve the adventure? She was fond of Auld Hoggard. Perhaps his opinion would help to sway her.

As he approached his house, doubts slowed Richard's stride. His home, no bigger than a weaver's quarters, meant happiness; and even more to Ann than to him, since it was all she had. His hand hesitated at the latch, but he drew it and walked in.

Before he could repent his purpose he announced, "Wife, I've a mind we should go to London."

A pretty round-faced young woman, with starched white cap and apron over a simple woolen dress, stayed the motion of her spinning wheel with one finger, and rose from beside the low hearth. She smiled, as though amused.

"Let me set your cloak to dry, Richard."

Richard's firm purpose showed signs of weakening. "But if you . . ."

"London? Why not? Do we go by sea, or overland?" Ann Hoggard reached up to unfasten the throat buckle, since Richard seemed unable to, and hung the cloak over a chairback.

"You are not surprised, wife? You are not afraid to venture?"

She gave a happy laugh. "It has been in your mind for three months past, and a score of times when you spoke of books or printing or schools your eyes turned southward. 'Twas only a matter of waiting for the egg to hatch, and the chick chirp London!"

His long arms clasped her plump little person to him. "Ann, tha'rt Angel!" He tried to mock his emotion by using broad Westmorland.

"Richard, tha'rt doited with years and book learning—

and damp beside!" She disengaged herself and smoothed
down her white apron. "The newcomers down the street
—De Rouville they're called—are in need of furnishings,
and will purchase ours for good value. I have spoken with
them already. Then there's this house. And if we do not
choose to carry money on our journey, de Rouville will
give us a bill upon his friends at York or London.
And . . ."

"And Richard Hoggard? What do you plan for him?"
Richard offered a mild protest at having his plans made
for him. "Do you take him with you?"

"Hoggard—whether it means Hog-guard or Hog-
ward—the name has grown dear to me. Yet is it seemly
that a man of letters should be so called?" She sounded
slightly breathless and her hands were wrinkling the
starched apron. "But 'tis for thee to say."

The family name was respected in the fells and dales,
and none had ever sought to change it. But Ann was
right. Strangers in a strange town might find it an object
of mockery. The hog-ward and his hog. Mistress Hog.
No, he could not let that happen. 'Twas the "hog" must
be altered.

"Haggard? Ann Haggard?" he experimented. But it
did not fit the buxom Ann. "Hoegard?"

"Ho-garth! It is near enough so that any old friends
who seek us will still find us."

"Mistress Ann Hogarth?" A wide grin spread across

Richard's solemn countenance. "A strange name, and stranger still that the two of us should meet. For my name too is Hogarth, Richard Hogarth. We must become better acquainted!"

BILLY HOGARTH'S LONDON

2: *The Reluctant Apprentice*

NOT FAR off now. He could hear the racket and hullabaloo of the Fair even above the racket and rumble of coach and wagons. The boy dodged beneath the nose of a drayhorse, was howled at by a teamster, eeled a passage between two quarreling milk-women . . . nearer and nearer to the enchanting roar. Then paused a moment to draw breath and to gaze.

Billy Hogarth was always stopping in the London streets to gaze and wonder. They were a continual pageant and fascination; each scene like something out of a play. As now. For above him and a little farther down the busy street a man leaned from an open window with a pole and hook. What was he fishing for? Oh, yes, that stroller below, with his hat off and wig uncovered. Skillfully the fisher angled for his catch. Below him the man, unaware, mopped his brow and started to replace his hat. But a moment too late. The hook caught in his ample wig. A sharp tug . . . the wig dangled a moment aloft, then

17

disappeared like a flash through the window. The owner of the wig—quite a good one, too, and new for it was almost white—stood vainly shaking his fist at the blank housefront above him.

No use his going to the door to report and protest. Before he could thud his cane on the door the thief would already have dodged out the back and be well on his way to the wig market in Monmouth Street. There was a lottery; tickets for the ordinary type wig sold for sixpence each, but for Grizzled Majors they were twenty-five shillings and Brown Bag wigs at fifteen; a fine bargain for the lucky holder of a winning ticket.

Billy let out a shout of laughter and sped on his way. London streets were filled with such excitement.

He was of an age when he had no thought but to accept the city as it existed, and for what it was; as an ocean that might be calm with peaceful strollers in the pleasure gardens or stormily destructive with its mobs surging to Tyburn or to protest against an unpopular movement of the rulers. But it was as useless to fear it as to hate. It was a force of nature, which not even the Lord Mayor or the King could alter; though 'twas said they tried to, as folk built embankments against a Thames' flood, but could not quell the daily tides.

Londoners preyed upon one another as pike fed upon trout, and sometimes the unwary duck as well. But Billy Hogarth was a London sparrow, and whoever heard of a pike catching a sparrow. He had no purse, no sword, no horse, no wig, nothing of worth, so was free to come and go unharmed since he had nothing to steal.

He was small for his fifteen years and very agile; leaping over the filthy channels that trickled down the centers of the narrow cobblestoned streets, dodging the irregular jutting housefronts, ducking beneath a broken inn sign that, loosened by the last windstorm hung askew from its bracket. The great carts and wains rumbled and clattered, streetmongers bawled their hundred wares, sang ballads or broke into fisticuffs. It was all wondrous and thrilling beyond belief.

And ahead lay St. Bartholomew's Fair.

As usual most of London seemed to be abroad in the streets, even those who like Billy Hogarth should rightly have been indoors. His father had left him to his Latin, while, with books beneath his arm, he had gone to correct proofs for a neighboring printer. Mother and the two little girls were busied in the kitchen at whatever women did busy themselves all day long. It was a warm day, the window was invitingly open. Who could resist it? Over the low sill and away.

Always, since he could remember, Father had tried to stop his constant attempts to escape lessons. He called it "running the streets" and as he said it, it sounded worse than being called a cutpurse or a highwayman. But it couldn't be wicked when joy bubbled up inside you and you saw a friend, or anyway someone you recognized on almost every corner.

This corner of London, near to St. Bartholomew's, was where the weavers had settled, as you could tell by the steady clack-clack of heddles, the regular thump-thump of batten on beam. Even had you been deaf as a post you'd have known by the street names, Cloth Fair and Cloth Court, and among these of old taverns and inns, long vanished, such as Rising Sun Court, Barley Mow Passage and Half Moon Court. The houses, wattle and daub, half-timbered as in the days of the Tudors, had escaped the Great Fire of 1666, and leaned their heads across the narrow passages, seeming to gossip of time long gone when London Town had lived almost entirely within its protecting walls. Now it was spreading outward, a rising tide, north and west, embracing moor and marsh and farmland as the lusty thriving population expanded year by year and the beginning of the Inclosure Acts deprived the country folk of wood and grazing ground, bringing them hopefully to London to seek new livelihoods.

But the weavers had been here for a hundred years and more; they were cockney born, though many still spoke their native tongue and the powerful Cloth Guild held a mort of Flemish members. There was a song they sang sometimes; they were singing it now, to the thump of the treadles.

"The weaver knows his shuttle
The shepherd knows his dog.
        Clack, clack, clack! Bow wow wow!"

Billy, whistling the catchy tune hurried on, past the open windows. He had heard it all his life, it was part of his very background. Father said once that the song might well have started long ago in Westmorland, his own country, since that was a land of shepherds and weavers.

He waved a gay hand at an idle apprentice lounging in an open door; who could blame a 'prentice for idling on such a fine, blue-skied day? Though one felt a twinge of envy for the apprentices, idle or otherwise. They were grown men almost, with an important Guild of their own. They belonged truly to London, were part of the pulse of the great city. It would be fine to be an apprentice, if one could choose one's trade. But not weaving, no, thank you, kind sir!

There ahead loomed the Goose and Tankard Inn. He was about to hurry past, but being Billy, halted at the scene before him. The York Coach, carrying passengers to the north, was about to depart, booted postillions and all. A great dark cave, the coach looked like, with gigantic wheels iron shod, and a row of steps leading up from the yard below. The driver in his great caped coat was struggling to assist through the narrow entrance an immensely fat woman. With his hand on her heaving buttocks he gave a great shove and a mighty shout of laughter.

On the sloping roof two men, seeking cheaper passage, had seated themselves precariously. How long, one wondered, could they keep their seats as the coach rocked and jolted its way over roads deep-pitted by the winter's floods?

Billy's father had often told of his own trip south from York, but he had traveled in one of the slower canvas-covered wagons, costing less, and stopped the night at miserable taverns along the way. Father said he had never seen London before that time, not till he was a man grown; a state difficult to imagine. Why, London was the whole world! Or at least its center.

Then Billy was around the corner, and all of a sudden the Fair lay before him.

This was Smithfield, for generations the center of England's great cloth market, and nowadays its greatest cattle market. Here, every Monday morning, came the cattle, sheep and pigs destined for the tables of London. In a whirlpool of stench and noise, a seething bellowing pande-monium of weary men and frightened animals; the drovers of Smithfield were reputed the most cruel and drunken of London's workers.

But for four days each summer the market was swept; booths of every sort and fashion went up around the walls of the yard, and the hucksters, showmen and thieves took over. It was a riotous period when almost anything might happen. Billy knew it well, from former years.

The folk were packed so tight you could scarce wriggle between 'em, and gazing upward, as they were, he gaped at a man crossing on a rope from one housetop to another, high against the sky. He was balancing his way as easily as a man might cross the street, likely even more so since there were no wagons to halt him. And right in the middle he paused to blow his nose with a mighty flourish. The crowd let out a gasp of avid horror. At any moment he might fall to the stones below!

There were a hundred sights to amaze one. Here and there, to the number of at least a dozen, scaffoldings held stages on which plays were being enacted, or about to commence. "See Jeptha's Rash Vow!" "See the Tall Dutchwoman!" shouted the barkers. "Come behold the Siege of Troy!" and all against the fine painted backdrops, which showed you plain as plain what Holland and old Troy really looked like. "Come see the horse with his head where his tail should be!" yelled another. Threading her way through the crowd came a female drummer; you'd think her a lady of the court, so full were her hooped skirts, so bare her bosom. By jumping into the air Billy could just get a glimpse of the strange little blackamoor with her, dressed in green and blowing a trumpet. It was said that many court ladies and even some of the more prosperous harlots kept such tiny black boys as pets; they were becoming mighty fashionable.

Cudgel players and wrestlers loudly vaunted their challenges, but would not come to blows until sufficient money was collected or at least in prospect. And there was a backsword player on horseback, his shirt and breeches already slashed from some earlier affray and of purpose left unpatched and unmended.

Now the shout went up for the Flying Man. There he stood, on the roof of the church beneath the bravely waving pennants. Three trumpet boys ran through the crowd taking offerings, a penny here, twopence there: all to see the man cast himself down from the tower, and instead of dashing to death on the stones beneath, fly like a bird to the window of the house across the wide yard.

Knowing Londoner that he was, Billy had seen the same trick at last year's Fair. The man had a notched bone or piece of horn strapped across his chest. He threw himself outward and down, along a barely visible cord so that the cord ran through the notch. So what he really did was only to slide face downward, like a boy on a snow slope, along the cord. Still, the act was a good one, and sometimes the rope broke.

The trumpeters must have collected enough money, for now a musket belched smoke from the church tower to announce the feat. The man cast himself down from the height and . . .

Billy felt a rude shove, and cannoned against a silken-clad young beau. The beau caught him angrily by the shoulder.

Billy shouted, "Watch your rump!"

But the cutpurse was too swift. He had snatched up the man's coattail, slashed the pocket with knife or razor, caught the leather purse deftly as it dropped. And was off through the crowd that was still peering aloft at the flying man. One of the oldest tricks in the world. An accomplice distracted the attention of the "gull," while the cutpurse did the deed. Billy had seen it a hundred times.

And even the beau seemed to know the trick, for with one hand he still grasped firm hold of Billy, with the other drew his toothpick of a sword, and shouted, "Thief here! Thief!"

It would have gone hard with Billy if a stranger had not come to his rescue. "Put up your sword, man. This boy is as innocent as you are. It was that rascally fellow over there in the brown coat; I saw him shove the lad."

"After him! Lay the villain by the heels!" The young beau plunged forward, but in hopeless confusion. For even if he caught the man the thief would have a dozen friends in this raffish mob to swear he had been quite somewhere else. And of course he would not be the one with the purse.

"Thank 'ee, Mister!" Billy breathed a sigh of relief. That had been a pretty close call, and he was certainly grateful.

The young man grinned down at him. It was difficult to place him, he was too old for a 'prentice; his shabby, yellowed wig wouldn't have fetched ten shillings, hardly five. He didn't wear a sword nor carry a tasseled cane, so he couldn't rightly be called a gentleman. Some patches of color, red and blue and even yellow which clung to his cuff gave Billy a clue, and his snub nose caught the odor of turpentine.

"You a painter, Mister?"

"I am. But how did you guess?"

Billy wanted to reward his rescuer. "There's a kind of

look in your eye, as though you were seeing right into people and things!"

"Ah, a fellow physiognomist, no less! I am indeed a painter. Some of my work"—he gestured toward the stage backdrops—"is here displayed."

Billy's jaw dropped. He gazed and gazed, wide-eyed. The man chuckled. "Seldom," he commented, "have I had a more appreciative public. Would you like to come back to my workshop? It's not far from here."

To see the workshop of a real artist? He had never hoped for anything so marvelous. All the wonders of the Fair, which anyway he had seen many a time before, faded before it.

He followed along and as they threaded their way through the streets and cut through alleys, Billy learned that the man's name was Hobson Wragg, that as well as painting theatre scenery he made signboards, and sometimes even limned a portrait.

They were hurrying westward, away from the Fair toward Clerkenwell, where the Hogarths themselves now lived. It was a relief to know that the artist dwelt in that direction, for though Billy had skipped away from his lessons, he still felt a prick of conscience and would prefer to reach home again before his father returned from the printer's. Clerkenwell, once a village, had grown vastly since the Great Fire, and now sprawled northward and ever northward, its greedy tentacles engulfing marsh and even farmland.

In fact painter Wragg's workshop turned out to be a derelict barn right at the edge of the marsh. Billy wrinkled his nose. You could smell the turpentine and also the varnish and oil even before the door opened; a strange smell, but somehow exciting.

Inside, the roof stretched upward past the old hayloft, and a window set into the gable let in extra light. This slanted down on two long stretches of canvas extending almost the length of the barn. On this had been sketched in charcoal and partly filled in with color an ancient ruined castle and a modern drawing room; future backdrops for some play no doubt. A pile of smoothed boards in one corner, cut into signboard length, long benches of colors in large clay pots, and a strong smell of rotten eggs—that would be for the tempera paints Billy knew —and a further confusion of things quite incomprehensible to his wondering eyes.

Before a long table a boy, younger than Billy and even skinnier, was sanding down a signboard on which showed a half-obliterated bull and sun. The boy glanced up, gave a welcoming grin, and went on with his work. An artist's apprentice perhaps?

But all this was a miracle. Ever since he could recall, Billy had been making small sketches on his slate or on the margins of his books, trying to capture the likeness of faces and figures he had glimpsed in the roaring London streets. He knew well how books were written and turned from manuscript into bound volumes; his father's work dealt with the printers' trade. But pictures and paintings were another thing. It seemed that they didn't just happen; someone drew them and painted them. Here indeed was the process right before his eyes.

For an hour or more he wandered around, fingering the dozens of brushes, touching the many colored powders that were mixed with oil and turpentine to form the paints, and listening to Wragg as he expounded, or instructed the boy about finishing off the new signboard. Then as the light through the window began to fade, he stammered his gratitude for so wonderful a finish to a day, and started homeward, all bemused. Wragg had asked him to come again. Yes, he would do that; the Fair no longer held forth temptation. How, if perhaps *he* could become a painter's apprentice?

In the next few weeks he began for the first time to put serious effort into his studies, so that no one would suspect how much time he spent in the painter's workshop. His former playground, the streets, no longer held the same fascination. Here at last was a chance for him to learn something about the trade of drawing and painting, and Wragg, flattered perhaps by so apt a convert, was kindly and generous in suggestions and criticism. He showed the boy not only how colors were ground and mixed to apply to the canvas, how cartoons were made in advance for enlarging to the great stage backdrops, but also how to lay out a composition.

This method, said Wragg, was achieved by something

called symmetry. You drew with charcoal a series of diagonal lines, equally distant and at right angles to each other
all across the canvas. Along these guide lines you sketched
in your figures, laying them out so that an arm or hand, a
leg or foot, or even a table or chair fell along the diagonal
lines. The result, he said, helped to form a pattern uncon-
sciously pleasing to the eye of the beholder, though at
times you had to distort the figure to get it to fit into this
symmetry.

Then one day, following the afternoon dinner, Richard
Hogarth exploded a bombshell. "Today, young William,
I have asked my friend Scarlette the printer if he will take
you on as an apprentice."

Billy paused in the doorway where he had been just
about to dodge off again to spend the evening hours with
Wragg. "Couldn't I," he put forth, "be apprenticed to
a painter?" Perhaps even Wragg might need another boy.

Richard shoved back from the table and regarded his
son with astonishment. "Painter? But the painters have
no Guild. You might be an assistant to an artist; a helper,
a servant. But never an apprentice, recognized as such."

Billy had already considered that argument. Apprenticeship was more than a training for a trade, for your life's
work. When you entered the house of your master you
left your own home behind and were almost adopted into
the new one. Your new master was like a parent, and a
stern one, too. You were fed with his own sons and daughters, and clothed as well. Since, to begin with, you were

not of much profit to your master, your own father had to pay down quite a large sum of money, and if you ran away that sum was forfeit. Also if you were caught—and the local papers often carried notices of such runaway apprentices—you were handed back and severely punished.

But when the seven years of your contract had run out, then your master took you before his Guild. If he spoke well of your industry, and you could show good specimens of your work, the Guild made you a journeyman, that is, a man who was hired by the *journee,* the day, for real wages. Thereafter you were almost certain of a profitable livelihood.

Father, as a teacher and, on the side, a translator and reader of proof for the printers had had no such security. People paid him for the work he did; or they omitted to do so. But he could do nothing about it. There was no powerful Guild behind him. No wonder he wanted something more stable for his only son.

Billy could realize that. But all the same . . .

His father regarded the boy with understanding. "Yes, I know; I was like you at one time, with ambitions of my own. Perhaps"—he hesitated—"there is Mr. Ellis Gamble in Leicester Fields, at the Sign of the Golden Angel. Perhaps he could turn your skill with the pencil to some account, though you are over old to start to learn all the secrets of the art of casting silver and gold work."

And so it turned out that he began his apprenticeship. Billy found that the first stages were the same as everywhere; fetching water from the pump down the street, sweeping, tending the annealing furnace in the shop, being dispatched for ale for the others. For a time he was indeed little more than a servant, sleeping on a straw pallet beneath the counter, rising as the bells of St. Mary le Bow rang out in the morning, and continuing with no letup till they rang again at nine of the evening. This curfew, or *couvre feu,* cover the fire, had come down from the days of the Normans. Most 'prentices considered the working hours overlong. There was an ancient jingle about it—and London was full of such jingles and songs—chanted at times by the boys in the shop. It was addressed to the bell ringer, *Clerk of the Bow Bell with yellow lockes. For thy late ringing thy head shall have knockes.*

Then came tasks slightly more skillful; collecting the silver dust and fine shavings from the cloths attached to the tables where the shapers and engravers sat, and melting these down into silver beads in the crucibles. Later he began sketching for some engraver whose sight had begun to fail. Then, his hand shaking so much from nervousness that he could scarcely guide it, being allowed his first chance to set a fine-pointed burin, as the silversmiths called it, to the gleaming silver, and begin to plow the hairbreadth lines in the precious metal itself.

The touch of the tool in his hand might have converted William Hogarth to being a silversmith for life. Engraving was creating, and there was something, a struggle, a pain, a delightful frenzy in trying to turn thought through the skilled hand and eye into those delicate lines, and make those lines render back to the beholder that same thought. This was being an artist.

But William Hogarth was almost a man, rising nineteen. Swaggering with his fellow 'prentices down the streets of London Town, which owned them and which by rights they owned.

Why not? The town, riotous, brawling, lusty, stank to high heaven. But with a stench to which they were well accustomed. Smoke rose from the thousands of soft-coal-burning fireplaces, forming a fog that coated the leaves of the trees, sifting a sooty rain on the garments of fine gentlemen and ladies. 'Twas a sign of wealth, that there should be so many fires and so much soot. What had once been streams, indeed the very roads themselves, were now open sewers and the contents of chamberpots were freely tossed from upper windows, followed more often than preceded by the shout of warning. Since many of the upper stories of houses projected over the roadway, this had given rise to the custom that a gentleman should walk nearer the gutter, on the outside, and the lady in the more sheltered position, beneath the overhang. Between gentlemen themselves there was often dispute as to the favored position; this led of right to blows, and often drawn swords.

Like the ocean itself William's London could be calm or stormy, more often stormy. Mobs rose easily, became almost uncontrollable, and were as suddenly calmed. You might see a hired bully jostle a gentleman of the court; they drew sword and fought, and one was wounded, or both were. Daily at Tyburn or at Newgate prison men were hanged, sometimes even someone you knew. A highwayman had the acknowledged privilege of being first to mount to the gallows, known as Tyburn Tree, and the right to declaim such a farewell speech as would bring tears to the eyes, or rouse a tumult of catcalls and jeers. It was more affecting by far than the mock scenes created by the play actors.

This was London, a free show for everyone. Why not? Why should London be otherwise? London was the pigs rooting in the filth of the roads, it was the bemuffed and beribboned beaux, the fine ladies in silks and satins being carried in their chairs to routs and balls at Court, or to one of the great houses along the river. London was a never-ending spectacle for those who lived here and loved it.

It was also a most wicked town. As countrymen poured in, seeking employment, no honest work was open; they joined the criminal classes to become cutpurses, harlots and the like. "Holland" gin was cheap and untaxed, and perhaps safer than the polluted water. A rash of distilleries, some said to the number of four million, had sprung up throughout the country and those too wretched or too poor to buy good food sought solace in the potent liquor. Now the older men looked back with nostalgia on the "peaceful age" of William II and Queen Anne, when religion and morality flourished and the gaols were nearly empty.

But with no wars, discharged soldiers were everywhere. A man might be knocked down and murdered on his own doorsteps for the few shillings in his pocket, and a prudent man did not venture forth, unarmed, after dark, for street lamps were few and far between. There were "thieves kitchens" where small childden were trained in the fine art of picking pockets. Wrongdoers who had money to bribe the watch or the law were ignored, or escaped with a caution, but lacking such funds you landed in prison, where you were left to rot or starve, or be deported, that is, sent abroad to the colonies in America or the plantations of the West Indies.

All such shows were part of young Hogarth's London, since all jails could be visited by sightseers; stocks, pillories and hangings were a part of the great town's amusements and even the madhouses were open to the public.

The streets, too, were full of spectator entertainment. The bearward strolled past, his moth-eaten and pathetic beast shambling behind on a lead chain attached to a nose-ring; the trouper with his blousy dancing girl set up his pitch with pipe and drum right outside the shop while the 'prentices rushed to the windows to watch. And as background music there were the constant shouts of street vendors, the endless rumble of carts and wains. The life blood of the city pulsed through the streets with whip-cracking wagoners and cursing coachmen, sedan chairs guarded by running footmen, bootblacks and chimney sweeps plying their trade, or the 'prentices pouring forth with clubs and fists to fight a rival Guild. Just for the sheer joy of youth and bodily combat.

Half a million men and women without a master, for even the King now lived outside the City. He was not permitted to enter with his soldiers save by permission of the Mayor himself. Where the Guilds were strict enough in the quality of their cloth, the purity of their silver, they cared nothing for life or death.

London stank, it rotted; it throve mightily, and was dearly loved.

How young Hogarth yearned to be able to set it all down on canvas! William, the silversmith's appentice, was in love with his London and would have made a likeness of his love. Had he been able.

But how could one compass London in one picture, or even in a thousand?

He was constantly sketching. There was for instance that incident in the alehouse. One Sunday he had set out with two fellow 'prentices for an excursion to the Highgate countryside. In the afternoon, hot and thirsty, they stopped at an alehouse, and as they drank, before their amused eyes two men started a brawl. One of the two, seizing his heavy tankard as a weapon, crashed it down on the other's head.

The crowd might laugh, or sympathize with the man,

his face contorted in pain, and blood coursing down from a deep scalp wound. But to William's ever-ready pencil and sketch book here was an absorbing model. The artist must record the event; he had no right to pass judgment upon it.

There was no hope of engraving such scenes on silver. But there were artists, a few, not many, who did engrave their pictures on copper from which not one but a hundred prints could be made. And better still perhaps—and William's fingers itched for them—were the brushes, the color-loaded palettes and well-stretched canvases of the true painters.

It was during this period of yearning for a new outlet that he discovered the majestic work of James Thornhill, recently knighted, and now Serjeant-painter to King George I. The work on the walls and vast dome of St. Paul's was somewhat akin to that of William's old friend, Hobson Wragg. But, oh, how different!

Those extravagant murals, yards and yards of them, swarmed with Roman senators in long white togas; allegorical graces and muses in billowing sun-touched robes posed against the cloud-filled skies, all mingled in scenes both classical and romantic. While overhead on the ceiling plump, beaming amorini waved ribbons and scarves against skies more sunny than ever smoky London saw.

This indeed was Art. It must be. For it was well-known that for every square yard of decorated wall Sir James was paid a guinea, and for the ceiling, which must

be a vastly more difficult task, no less than three guineas
for the same amount of space. Though much of this was
only plain pink or blue.

Then on a day, which gave sudden point and purpose
to his intentions, his hopes and longings, William saw
the great Thornhill himself, at work in St. Paul's.

This chance encounter was to have a momentous result; not only with regard to Hogarth's work, but concerning his life. For Sir James had a daughter, a demure
little girl of seven or eight. She stood quietly gazing at
the paintings while her mother, in wide hooped skirt,
lace apron and lace cap beneath the wide "milkmaid"
hat, chatted with the great painter. Lady Thornhill was
every inch the wife of a prosperous artist and merchant of
paint by the square yard. One would scarcely have noticed
her small daughter. William Hogarth, from his vast age
of nineteen or twenty, certainly did not.

3: *William Tilts at his First Windmill*

LONDON WAS changing, though perhaps only in the mind and eyes of young William Hogarth. Now that he was one of the senior apprentices and the day drew near when his endenture would expire he must give serious thought to what his future would be. No longer could he rush forth from his master's shop at the cry of "Clubs! Clubs!" and join in some glorious, youthful free-for-all against apprentices of a rival Guild. The hangings of notorious highwaymen at Tyburn had become almost too commonplace to be worth attending. The whippings of habitual whores at the cart's tail before they were dragged off to Newgate prison, or even the pelting with rotten eggs and street filth of cutpurses penned in the pillories was no longer a comical sight.

As a journeyman of his Guild he would be a responsible citizen of the town, could be called upon if need be to bear arms in the train band, and later, to undertake any one of a score of civic duties. But did he really want to be a journeyman silversmith? True, the silversmiths' was one of the most honored and respected of the City

Guilds, the employment clean and respectable, and certainly one that Richard Hogarth would have approved. But it was also precarious. Civil war or foreign war silenced the silvery ring of the hammers; for silverware, like gold, was bought when times were peaceful and prosperous, but when times grew hard it was melted down for money.

Nobody melted down a painting. The finest work of the silversmith, even of Benvenuto Cellini himself, might end up as a handful of ill-stamped coins, and those coins in turn, a generation or so later, be turned back into bowls and platters. But with a painting now, the older it was the greater its value, no matter how miserable a daub. Or so it seemed.

Next best to being a painter, working in color, would be to become an engraver. Not on silver, but on copper, from which many prints could be made. The prints might prove more durable than the silver, unless fated to wrap a fresh fish or a pound of butter.

If his father had been alive the choice of a trade might have been more difficult. But soon after the family moved back to Long Lane, to the neighborhood of Bartholomew's Close, Richard Hogarth fell ill and died. There was not sufficient money to furnish a dowry for Mary and Ann, still in their teens, but both girls, like their mother, were skilled needlewomen. So they opened a small millinery shop in the front room of the house, where dress materials from Milan were displayed or made up to the customer's order. William often dined with this cheerful family group, but he was not yet paid enough to be of any financial aid, nor in fact would he be free to live at home until his seven years of apprenticeship had been served.

Surprisingly the little Hogarth shop was a success. The three women began to purchase more material "dimmity and flanel" and to make a small reputation for fine honest workmanship. And as the time drew near for William to leave Ellis Gamble at the Sign of the Golden Angel in Cranbourne Street, he engraved a small shop card, or business card for his master. Then he made another for himself, *W. Hogarth, Engraver,* embellishing it with garlands, cupids, an anonymous goddess and nymph, and a formidable bearded personage, perhaps Art or Science, engraving or writing. This broke it to Gamble what his intentions were for the future.

His mother and sisters would have had him return to Long Lane. As a journeyman silversmith, he no longer had to live under Gamble's roof. But now that he had decided to be an engraver and even had ambitions toward painting, he needed room to spread out his tools. The copper sheets on which he graved the shop notices were small, the tools were few, and he could work on any bench or table if the light were good. But a painter needs room to grind and mix his colors, to stretch and prepare his canvases, to seat his models should he have commissions for portraits, and a safe place to store wet paintings.

In the flurry and fluff of a busy dress shop this was impossible.

So William visited the barbers and had his head properly shaved, and was fitted for a wig. Not a new one, of elegant curled white horsehair, but a somewhat yellowed second-hand one. All the same it was a certain sign of his manhood and emancipation. Perhaps the wig brought him to the attention of Lady Luck, for almost immediately she cast him a smiling glance. In addition to the shop notices he had drawn and engraved he had tried his hand at a satirical print of the money madness of the famous South Sea Bubble, which had burst so disastrously to the ruin of many speculators the year before. The prints, displayed in the window of one of his father's publisher-printer friends, drew considerable attention and had an excellent sale. At last William could begin to add to the small savings from his apprentice days.

It was in this joyous mood, in fine full wig and new blue coat with huge pockets, that he strolled across London Bridge. And again Lady Luck was friendly; his eye fell on a notice offering a room for rent. This was in the attic of a tall house on the east, the downriver side of the Bridge. The light was excellent for his purpose, the room generous enough for a workshop; promptly he paid down the coins for a quarter-year's lease, then went home to report his new independence.

London Bridge was typically London, yet not the London he had grown up in. The houses that lined it solidly on both sides were, some said, "stately palaces," five or six stories in height and leaned out over the river as well as forming an arcade over the busy bustling street far below. At one end stood the small Chapel of St. Thomas of Canterbury, for this was the road that pilgrims once took to the holy shrine of St. Thomas. At the other end, topping Traitor's Gate mounted on pikes as they blackened in the sun and rain, were the heads of those beheaded for treason. And far down, when the tide was at ebb, State barges, watermen and lighters fought for right of way through the dangerous rapids that swirled between the wide piers, bawling and shouting curses at one another in their own special language. For more than any rutted roadway in England, the broad Thames was the artery of London. Market produce flowed downstream on its bosom, to provision the ships of the King's navy, or the merchantmen bound for the West Indies and colonies of North America, and from the ships in the Pool below the bridge came all manner of raw materials from abroad.

Here, at the northern entrance of London Bridge gangs and confidence tricksters lay in wait for simple country-men from Kent or Surrey. Hogarth's sober respectable garb, obviously that of a Londoner, would make him safe from press gangs and confidence men, but he car-ried always a stout stick, nearer to a 'prentice's cudgel than to a beau's tasseled cane. It was even surer protec-tion than a gentleman's sword.

Now, with growing prosperity, Mary and Ann Hogarth and their mother considered moving their small shop to a more favorable location, and William set to work to design them a business card. It was a true labor of love, and he could not help making the simple announcement into a little story-telling picture: Auld Hoggard's mantle had fallen upon the shoulders of his nephew.

The card was no mere lettered announcement of the opening of the new business, but showed a well-furnished shop interior, shelves reaching to the ceiling, a pretty chandelier, and a minute scene. Husband and wife had brought their tiresome fattish youth to be outfitted with a new coat.

Below this the announcement read

MARY AND ANN HOGARTH from the old Frockshop the corner of the Long Walk facing the Cloysters . . . have now removed to ye KING'S ARMS joining to ye Little Britain gate, near Long Walk . . . and there sell ye best & most fashionable Ready Made Frocks sutes of Fustian, Ticken & Holland, stript Dimmity & Flañel Waistcoats, blue and canvas Frocks & bluecoat Boys Drars. Likewise Fustians, Tickens, Hollands, white stript Dimtys & stript Flañels in ye piece by Wholesale or Retale, at Reasonable Rates.

But before he could set up as a painter he must earn a living. For like his father, the thrifty north countryman, he had to be able to jingle two coins in his pocket before he could part with one. So, in his new studio above the busy traffic of the river and the jostling carts and travelers on the bridge, he set himself to engrave more business cards.

A second goldsmith, William Hardy in the Radcliffe Highway, announced himself to the public on one of Hogarth's cards. As advertisements, of any shop from an Italian warehouse to a tobacconist, prints from Hogarth's copperplate engravings were profitable both to merchant and artist.

But such hack work was not enough. Through his father's connection with the printer-booksellers William found a more ambitious outlet for his growing skill. Compared with honest merchants they were poor business risks, but what William now needed was prestige. His engraved illustrations of *The Travels of Aubrey de la Mottraye,* and of *The Golden Ass (The New Metamorphosis),* were, in a sense, his own business cards.

Guild training had made him a skillful engraver. But again, this was not enough. Wherever Hogarth's blunt inquisitive nose and short eager legs led him through the town, pencil and paper went with him. Not content with sketching, he sharpened his perception by a self-taught system of memorizing types of noses, of eyes, of wigs and details of costume. Characteristic postures and movement of any kind had a special appeal to him. It was generally said that no artist could ever hope to portray a person or object in motion; but here was an artist who believed he could.

Yet earning a living and learning to see and record were only, he felt, an apprenticeship to the master craft of painting in oils. Sir James Thornhill continued to be his idol, and he returned again and again to study that artist's work wherever he could find it.

A school for art students had recently been opened in St. Martin's Lane by John Vanderbank and Louis Cheron. Hogarth was probably one of the first to join it. Such a class offered the chance to work at leisure from a posed model, often in the nude. It also offered the fellowship of other young artists—and, to a craftsman in any line of work, to discuss his love, his art, is as important as to labor at it.

Here it was that he first encountered William Kent. A tall, square, ruddy-faced man, considerably older than Hogarth, dropped in one evening not to study or work from the model, but to air his own views.

Loudly he proclaimed the superiority of the Italianate school of painting, boasted of his long studies in Italy, of his own ability, and of the many designs and paintings he was engaged in. Hogarth wondered why John Vanderbank bowed and scraped so low instead of showing the crass and noisy intruder the door.

Leaning over the shoulder of one of the pupils, Kent

grunted his contempt in broad Yorkshire. "Tha's only a dauber, lad. Tha's English so tha'lt never be a painter." And offering no helpful hints, but leaving despondency in his wake, moved on and paused behind Hogarth.

Before William could prevent it the man's heavy arm reached over his shoulder and a thick broad thumb scraped down through the charcoal sketch, blurring it beyond repair. And the arrogant voice advised, "Go back to tha trade of chimney sweep. Tha'll ne'er be aught else."

As quick-tempered as the next man, Hogarth would have jumped to his feet. But John Vanderbank laid a restraining hand on his shoulder. "William Hogarth shows considerable promise, Mr. Kent. He is already an engraver of some importance."

"Tombstone letterer, belike!" William Kent gave an ill-natured chuckle.

Hogarth tried to repair his drawing, but his shaking hand only made it worse. As soon as the class ended he made a point of asking who the well-dressed boor might be.

William Kent had begun as modestly as he had himself. As assistant to a coach painter the country boy had shown enough promise for a group of Yorkshire gentlemen to send him to Italy to study, and had supported him for the past ten years. As well as copying Italian masters he had collected Italian paintings and antiques for his patrons.

Now the great Lord Burlington had "discovered" him, and haled him back to England. Somehow this painter of only mediocre ability had imposed himself on the gullible public as a man of all-round genius who, like the late Sir Christopher Wren or even the unique Leonardo da Vinci, could turn his hand with equal mastery to painting, architecture, landscape gardening or even designing ladies' dresses. Titled patrons competed for his favor, and to all of them he was equally and profitably rude.

'Twas no wonder he had lorded it over a handful of art students and their teacher!

Kent's specialty had been, and still was, the copying of Italian masterpieces, which suited him well, since Italian Masters were the cult of the day. Young lords on their continental tours loaded themselves with real or imitation Italian Masters, great brown-stained canvases to decorate the enormous stairways and corridors of their country mansions. Old Masters had taken the place of tapestries for this purpose. Anyone could turn them out, and almost any artist did. It seemed that the age of the painting was what mattered most to the easily duped public, which if it could not purchase the genuine article, rushed to pay good money for something just as large, as faded, as brown, no matter how badly painted.

Hogarth's admiration of the genuine painters of Italy and Holland, the real Old Masters, was as strong as his contempt for the imitators and copyists. To his mind there was as great a gulf between these uncreative hacks and such artists as Sir James Thornhill. True, his giant allegorical figures might be un-English in posture and garb, his skies of a cerulean blue that never smiled upon smoky London, but they were no slavish copies, and to a fellow-artist every brushstroke signed his honest name. Perhaps some day English painters might paint England, as Van Steen and other Flemish painters had depicted their own land and people. But so long as the Italianate craze persisted there would be no sale for such work.

It was nearly two years since William had seen his old friend Hobson Wragg. An errand took him back to Clerkenwell, and, seeing the studio door, newly painted, the old barn freshly whitewashed, he knocked and went in. Wragg was no longer the lean and hungry young painter. He held out a plump hand in welcome, and drew William into the busy workshop. Not only had he the same apprentice William recalled from earlier days, but two others were hard at work. It seemed as though painting stage scenery brought in better money these days, or else Wragg had found a market for his other work.

Hogarth gazed about the walls. Where now were the towers of ancient Troy? Where, indeed, the tumblers and actresses he had once tried to depict? The long strips of canvas had all disappeared. Instead, glistening in their new varnish, hung a dozen or more "Old Masters."

Wragg nodded toward them with a grin. "What d'you

think of them, William? Of course they aren't smoked or torn and repaired yet, and that's what really counts." He slapped his thigh and gave a roar of laughter. "There's more to painting, Billy, than I ever dreamed—like the manure pile outside in which I season my canvases, to yellow and rot them."

Amused, despite himself, Hogarth had to listen to more tricks of the trade. Wragg, it seemed, laid out the pictures in charcoal, painted in the heads and bodies, and left his assistants to supply the backgrounds, landscapes, draperies, curtains and similar effects. "We can do six of an average size in a week. We get more for the square foot than your friend Thornhill does for his murals, and the agent sells for up to five times what he pays me. Mind you, I don't say it's honest; but it's safer than sheepstealing!"

Sick at heart Hogarth returned to his studio perched above the Thames. Wragg was an old friend, the first to help and encourage him. Yet he felt as though Wragg were betraying him. Perhaps it wasn't his friend's fault. When enough people wanted bad gin, instead of good ale and wines, distillers by the thousand would supply them. And that was what was happening to painting.

Were there no rules to the craft such as there were to silversmithing, in which a man must give value in honest work and even in the weight and purity of silver? Wragg's painting was not even honest copying to be sold as such, and the seasoning of the canvas, the smoking, the tears and deliberate patching were all intended to make the picture pass for an antique.

No silversmith would kick his work about the floor to give it spurious value, and if he punched false hallmarks on it he would be fined by his Guild, and might even have his ears cropped by the common hangman. But there were no deterrents for Hobson Wragg, no punishments awaiting the even more venal William Kent.

From his earliest days William Hogarth had felt the need to sketch and paint. He felt he had a gift, and knew he had developed an ability. But could a man make a living from honest painting?

Discouraged but obstinate he returned to his work. They were mostly portraits these days when he could find a paying sitter. His craftsmanship was sound, and the results had charm. From these developed his "conversation pieces," small canvases in which a group of figures sat naturally about a table, or posed a little more formally on a lawn against a distant landscape. Action could be presented by players on a stage, so why not by a painter on canvas? His novel aim resulted in such works as *The Wantead Assembly* in which groups of figures moved in a charming dance.

He followed these up with other groups, resembling the homely scenes which the Dutch painters of the seventeenth century loved to depict. But *Lord Hervey and His Friends, The Wedding of Stephen Beckingham and Mary Cox* and others were as typical of Hogarth as the scenes were English.

He would learn, but he would not imitate. Nor would he be a mere "phiz-monger" who ran a small portrait factory in which the artist himself painted only the faces, leaving his assistants to fill in the fashionable silks, satins and laces of the sitter's costume. This practice of depicting his sitters in their home surroundings was to prove of value to him later. In no other way could a humble artist have penetrated into the homes of the wealthy, and become familiar with interiors in which great mirrors threw back the reflection of fine furniture and Italian cut-glass chandeliers—vistas which he was later to use as freely in his story pictures as the everyday scenes of London streets.

But more than anything at the moment Hogarth wanted to show movement, not the standard static posed portraits. His conversation pieces gave scope for this novelty. A gentleman raises a delicate glass to his lips and is about to drink. A lady flirts her fan. A child points her toe in the first movement of a dance, or plays with her toys.

The young artist was especially successful with his portraits of children, capturing their gaiety and light-hearted innocence. But all his work brought less satisfaction than before. The prices he could charge brought him less profit than did the sale of the many prints which could be taken from each engraving. Painting just for painting's sake would lead him nowhere, unless he followed the lead of Kent and Wragg and catered to the taste for the Italianate, with all its trickeries and impostures.

But there was one artist whose work he could afford to admire. Thornhill's murals were the man's own work. They had to be. Even had he wished he could not have pretended that a whole wall of a church was the work of some Old Master and had just been brought over from Italy. Others must have shared Hogarth's honest admiration, for Sir James Thornhill was forced to open a class for students in the workshop behind his dwelling in Middle Covent Garden. William Hogarth became a pupil.

To his surprise, Sir James already knew some of his engravings. Not only had Hogarth the satisfaction of receiving instruction from a noted artist but he was allowed to assist practically in the execution of his frescoes. This was a new art to Hogarth, using different paints, fresh techniques and the knack of proportional enlargement from the small cartoon sketch to the wide spaces of wall or ceiling. Meanwhile he continued to sell prints from his engravings and to illustrate a few more books.

No longer a struggling student, but not yet prosperous, William bought himself a sword, the symbol of a gentleman. Just as earlier he had marked the beginning of independent adult life by assuming a wig. In his diary he set down how once he had gone moping to the city with scarce a shilling in his pocket, but on the receipt of ten guineas for an engraved plate he had gone home, put on his sword, and sallied forth again with all the confidence of a man with ten thousand pounds in his pocket.

A man with wig and sword could no longer mingle unnoted with the London crowds as the London sparrow had done. Nor, like a carefree apprentice, could he any longer take the town and its laughter and misery, its kindness and cruelty, for granted. A cutpurse was a threat to his ten guineas, a wig-snatcher endangered his wig. He was no longer an amused neutral observer of the harsh struggle for existence in the streets he loved so well.

A sneak thief tried to rob a legless soldier who begged outside St. Paul's; but the beggar swung his crutch, and the thief went off hugging a broken arm. A serving girl ran away from an Alderman's wife, but was brought back and punished. The girl died from the beating, or some said from starvation. A man thrashed his horse to death since it could no longer draw its load and the wagoner was drunk. With no means left to earn a living the wagoner became a footpad, and was shot and killed.

Was London the new Sodom and Gomorrah as some said? Not to William Hogarth. Yet he could no longer accept it as one huge boisterous joke, nor as something inevitable like storm or fire or an apprentice's pimples. Hogarth the Painter began to observe his world of luxury and filth, of wealth and poverty, of lords, criminals and proud craftsmen with a more discerning eye. The Londoner and the artist were to become the critic.

Hogarth's knack of graphic satire had a more immediate victim. At the school he heard more of William Kent, partly from Sir James' son, John Thornhill, with whom Hogarth had struck up a friendship. As Court Painter to the Crown, a more important rank than Thornhill's as Serjeant-painter, Kent's arrogance and pretensions were an affront to any honest artist, and the increasing demand for his work proof positive of the depths to which English taste had sunk.

It was rumored about the school, and also in the Thornhill home where Hogarth now dined quite frequently with Lady Thornhill, John and his fourteen-year-old sister Jane, that a big commission was to come Sir James' way. No less than the decoration of the Cupola Room in Kensington Palace. The pupils rejoiced, for in their view none but Sir James was equipped to carry out so important a task; and it could scarcely fail to lead to further Royal orders. Then came the blow. At the last moment Lord Burlington and other court favorites exerted their influence and snatched away the coveted honor. And who was to enjoy the fame and profit? William Kent!

The other pupils raged, but could do nothing. Hogarth felt that he could. And as a friend of the Thornhills it became his duty.

His satirical prints were already well known, and continued to find a good market. Such prints were displayed in the windows of the popular printer-booksellers, and always attracted considerable attention. Hogarth had a gift for depicting and caricaturing well-known public characters, from judges to highwaymen. In a sense they were topical newssheets, and the appearance of a new print by William Hogarth would attract gentlemen and artisans alike, to peer into the windows, laughing and exclaiming as they identified the likenesses, and often entering to buy. So popular had such prints become that they were often copied by less skilful engravers, the plagiarization skimming some of the cream from Hogarth's profit.

William Hogarth's opening shot was called *The Man of Taste*. It was a blunderbus load, which hit both Kent and his chief supporters. The scene was the redecoration of Burlington Gate, which gave the public an obvious clue to the identity of the man, described in the scroll at the bottom as a laborer, who climbed the scaffolding with a hod of mortar on his shoulder. On top of the gate a figure with brush and palette perched on a pediment labeled with the letters K.N.T., and lorded it over two recumbent figures to right and left labeled Raphael and Michael Angelo. Another figure on the scaffolding is described as "P. A plasterer, whitewashing and bespattering." The poet Pope, who had vilified his last patron as grossly as he now glorified the Earl of Burlington, was as easily recognizable as Burlington the plasterer, and Kent exalting himself above the great Italian painters.

At a shilling each, the usual price of such prints, they had a wide popularity. And Pope, a bitter little man, became Hogarth's enemy for life. What Kent thought, we do not know.

Shortly after this, Hogarth gave William Kent another sharp prick with his burin. The Church of St. Clement Danes ordered an altarpiece from the Court Painter at a cost of sixty pounds. The result was such a wretched careless painting that the angry parishioners forced the Bishop of London to order its removal. Later it is said to have been occasionally borrowed to decorate an alehouse.

Hogarth lit into the daub and the famous dauber with characteristic glee. His engraving purported to depict, in Hogarth's own words, "Ye celebrated altar peice in St. Clement's Church." The print reduced Kent's painting of a celestial choir to a tangle of ungainly limbs, most of them out of drawing, with a key of letters drawing attention to the shortest joint and longest joint of an angel, and a leg "but whether the right or left is yet to be discovered," and noting that the other leg had been judiciously removed to make room for the angel's harp.

The heated controversy which had already raged over the original painting resulted in considerable sales of this rather blunt skit upon it.

Hogarth must have been an eager theatre goer, for his first satire on public taste deplored the neglect of the classical playwrights, from Shakespeare to Congreve, and the current preference for trashy pantomimes, masquerades; and of course the Italian Opera with its imported singers, which corresponded closely with the Italianate art which he so detested.

Londoners had always loved the theatre, and in Shakespeare's day he and his contemporaries wrote for and played to a wide cross section of the population. Later the Puritan suppression of all amusements had broken the tradition of the English stage. Cromwell's death and the Restoration under Charles II had revived theatregoing, but mainly as an amusement for the Court, the upper classes and their footmen. Perhaps as a consequence the bulk of the plays turned upon the theme of a wife deceiving her husband, with such eighteenth-century titles as *The Careless Husband, She Wou'd or she Wou'd Not, The Fashionable Lover, Three Hours After Marriage.*

The price of seats was much the same as in the time of King Charles. Boxes, which were on the stage itself, cost four shillings, the pit half a crown, and the galleries one shilling and sixpence to one shilling. When actors, and particularly popular actresses, demanded better pay, up to four pounds a week, a manager tried to raise the price of seats. The footmen in the gallery rioted, tore up the seats, threw bricks and soot until management conceded they should pay only a shilling as before. But box and pit prices were raised—perhaps because such seats belonged to less objectionable customers.

All plays were given at night, and there were no matinées. In the intervals the beaux of the day strolled about, purchasing oranges or apples from the pretty vendors, took snuff, and discussed the latest actress or the lead's approach to his part of hero. Though there were only two theatres, the limited class from which the audience was drawn made long runs impossible, and a play which lasted ten nights drew smaller and smaller houses. For prosperous, vital, crowded London took no interest in the contrived and vapid performances.

But now, on to this scene of empty elegancies burst a truly English opera, the like of which had never been seen before. It cast all conventions aside. It dealt with cutpurses and highwaymen and their molls, the hangings at Tyburn, the inside of Newgate Prison, and all the criminal riffraff of London's streets. It was fresh, it was lusty. It was an instant and lasting success. Its catchy traditional airs were sung in London streets, and were to be sung for generations.

Its name, of course, was *The Beggar's Opera*.

John Gay had drawn London's portrait upon London's stage, and Londoners who had never entered a theatre before flocked to see it. For much the same reason that citizens and passing apprentices had stopped to gaze in printers' windows when Hogarth's prints were exhibited. They could recognize the characters in *The Beggar's Opera,* or others just like them. They knew the underworld heroes and their thieves' cant.

For in London of the early 1700s the law-abiding and the lawless rubbed shoulders daily in the narrow streets. Certain inns were notorious hangouts for highwaymen like Captain MacHeath in the *Opera.* Highwaymen were dashing figures and free spenders, so what more likely than that MacHeath should have two girls on his hands? Low-class bawds frequented alehouses to invite unwary countrymen away and rob them in their sleep. Every 'prentice knew of a neighboring "fence" where servants—and sometimes dishonest 'prentices too—could get money for handkerchiefs, snuffboxes, wigs, hats, swords, ruffles or pocketbooks.

You couldn't live in London without seeing some of the criminals at work, you knew the word in thieves' cant for their special "lay." There were buffers, caddees, duffers, sharpers, smugglers, kiddies, crimps, divers, grabbers, shoulderers, and as many others as there were names for cordwainers, fletchers, hammermen and butchers in honest trade. You were lucky if you did not know from personal experience that watch officers and prison wardens could be as dishonest as the criminals themselves.

Peachum in the *Opera* was said to be Jonathan Wild. Now there was a wicked man! He organized half the crime in the city, and when he saw fit he betrayed his

own men. That was what took the gay Jack Sheppard
to the scaffold, though he escaped from Newgate twice.
But Jonathan Wild was hanged at last, the dirty nark,
and drew the biggest crowd ever seen at Tyburn.

MacHeath might be Jack Sheppard. Polly Peachum,
Lucy, and minor roles could all be identified, correctly or
not, with well-known London characters, alive or dead.
Week after week *The Beggar's Opera* played to rapt, full
houses, including Hogarth.

As a citizen of the town he could roar with laughter
and come close to tears. But the play was more to him
as an artist than a wildly popular romanticizing of low
life. It did what, according to his father, Auld Hoggard
had done in a small way back in Westmorland. It did
what he himself had been attempting to do with his
graving tools and brushes, in his conversation pieces and
satires, and even in his business cards. It portrayed reality,
as Auld Hoggard had done. And it held a mirror to
William Hogarth's beloved London.

Could an artist, limited to the two dimensions of his
static canvas or copperplate, do what the *Opera* had
achieved? The dream persisted.

In 1726 William Hogarth engraved the illustrations—
and issued separate prints besides at his own cost—of
Hudibras, by Samuel Butler. Somewhat after the fashion
of *Don Quixote,* it was full of ridiculous and humorous
situations. Hogarth's graving tools turned the characters

into contemporary Londoners. The scene called the *Burning of the Rumps* showed the well-known Temple Bar, with two traitors' heads and a leg on it, cobbled pavements, wooden balconies and swinging street signs such as he saw every day around him.

None the less the illustrations for *Hudibras* established him as an illustrator. He was already known as a portrait painter. But when an upholsterer, Joshua Morris, refused to pay for the tapestry-panel designs he had commissioned from Hogarth he based his defense on the grounds that Hogarth was no artist, but a mere engraver.

No despiser of money, and conscious of his reputation and dignity, William Hogarth went to law to extract the thirty pounds agreed upon. He brought forth a number of witnesses to attest his professional standing, among them his teacher Vanderbank and Sir James Thornhill himself. William Hogarth won his case, and silenced his critics.

In giving evidence in Hogarth's suit Sir James was repaying his debt for his pupil's satire on William Kent over the Great Cupola Room Commission. But the link between the two friends was much closer than that. Hogarth had recently assisted Sir James on several projects, including his grandiose murals. The latest collaboration had been on a large canvas entitled *The House of Commons*. Hogarth was by now almost a member of the Thornhill family. This was in 1728.

Had Hogarth's case been heard in the following year, it is doubtful if he could have called so eminent a witness, as by then they were not on speaking terms. For in 1729 William Hogarth eloped with Sir James' demure little daughter, Jane Thornhill.

4: The Newlyweds

THE CHURCH lay in the charming little village of Paddington, on the northeast outskirts of London. Jane herself had suggested the village, since it had once been Lady Thornhill's home, and Jane had known it from childhood.

William, waiting for the hackney coach to arrive, gazed about the village green with its grazing sheep, then without thinking fumbled in his pocket for paper and pointed lead. No paper, no pencil. Never since he could recollect, had he been without them. He began a frantic search for these constant tools of his trade, then remembered that he must have left them in his workday clothes, and today was no day for working.

Reassured, he adjusted the hang of his smart sword, cocked his tricorn more jauntily on his new white wig, then produced a large handkerchief with which to wipe his brow.

It was natural that Sir James should have set himself against the proposed match between his only daughter and a painter, who at thirty-one had yet to make a name for himself. Lady Thornhill, a trifle more encouraging, had still counseled patience. But if she got wind of the intended elopement might she not put a stop to it?

Then, heedless of dignity, wig, and past anxiety William leaped down the church steps, for swinging round the corner came an old-fashioned hackney coach with perforated iron shutters, shabby with years, but its two horses at a gallant trot, and one even wore a nodding rose in its headband.

The coach stopped. Hat beneath his arm, William wrenched open the door and offered his hand.

And out backed a strange female . . . no, when she turned it was Betsey, Jane's little maid.

Before he had really recovered, out stepped Jane herself, fresh as a June rose, and demurely mocking. "But, Billy, did you not expect me?"

His beaming glance had to assure himself that here was his love, and his good fortune. She was nineteen, with a delightful, slightly rounded face and lovely eyes— and fortunately not tall, since William himself was little over five feet. Confidingly she put her hand in its small lace mitt on William's arm, and with a smile suggested, "Should you not tell the coachman to wait, so that he may carry us down to the river?"

With a deferential touch to his hat and a broad smile the man climbed down from his box. "And you'll be needing a second witness, sir, I have no doubt. 'Twon't

be the first time I've, as you might say, officiated." And
he whistled up a boy to the horses' heads.

Now the Vicar appeared from inside the church and
stood waiting. He made no last-minute demur, but performed the simple ceremony, reminded them and their
witnesses to sign the register, accepted his fee and saw
them to the coach.

William Hogarth was slowly recovering his equanim-
ity. Jane must have received her mother's consent, if not
actual approval, for she had brought her maid, and it
seemed now that Betsey was coming with them. Then,
as the coach creaked and jolted over the rough Tyburn
road down toward the Thames, he found fresh cause for
worry.

"It is only the top floor of the house that I've been able
to rent. But there should be room for Betsey too."

Jane giggled, and patted his hand reassuringly. "I
trust though that the big room has a good northern light
for you to work by, Billy."

Indeed it had. A suitable workroom was the first thing
he had sought. Particularly since now he had a wife to
support. And her maid as well, it seemed. But he had the
grace to look confused.

The new Mrs. Hogarth appeared to catch his thought.
"What a bad bargain you have made of me, Billy. For
it all happened just as you said it would. Father must
have been suspicious; last evening he called me into his

study and warned me that I would have neither dowry nor portion if I married without his consent. So your Jenny comes to you quite penniless, and without even a wardrobe save what she has on her back." She gave a little sigh and smoothed down the silk of her wide skirt.

"Who are you to talk of bad bargains?" Hogarth pretended sternness. "See what you have thrown away, and all for a husband who owns nothing but the tools of his trade. Compared with you, I am a usurer."

And they laughed together. For who could take such cares seriously when even the London skies had turned blue for them; when the road was green on every side and sparsely traveled. Today was Wednesday; it was only on Monday that the mobs, avid for amusement, surged to Tyburn for the hangings.

The shabby hackney might have been the Lord Mayor's gilded coach, and it was a pity when on the north bank of the Thames they must pay if off and let it go, to transfer to the ferry. It was quite a task to persuade the timorous Betsey that crossing the river would not land them in Africa, or among the savages of the American colonies and that she would suffer neither gales nor shipwreck on the way. They were rowed to Lambeth stairs.

Jenny, resolved on immediate economy, decreed that they should complete the journey on foot. The little maid lagged mutinously behind until a wild duck rose quacking from the willow marshes. "Lawks a' me!" she squealed, and pressed more closely upon the heels of her new master with his reassuring sword.

But Jane's gallant purpose, to brave poverty and perhaps starvation by William's side, found little outlet. The top floor in the house he had chosen was adequate for their need. The village of Lambeth, which had grown up around the ancient palace of the Bishop, was cleaner and far less noisy and riotous than Covent Garden. Each morning, mistress and maid sallied forth with basket to do their marketing, leaving William to work his long hours, till dusk, in his studio. And it was only two days before there occurred the hoped-for visit.

An imposing carriage and pair drew up before the new home. Jane, excited, called William to the window.

"It's Mother! She's found my note! I knew she would come. And look, she's brought my wicker trunk. Oh, I do hope she is not too angry!"

If Lady Thornhill was put out by having to make the long journey round by London Bridge and Southwark to visit her erring daughter, she gave no sign of it. She returned William's greeting with formal courtesy, and accepted Jane's rapturous embrace with a smile, then, perceiving her daughter's obvious happiness, began to unbend.

"Foolish children!" she chided them gently. "You should have heeded my advice and waited a little longer. Sir James is exceedingly angry, and will be yet more angry when he hears of my visit here."

So Lady Thornhill was still on their side, still wished them well, and had even braved Sir James to come to them. Yet William could almost sympathize with his father-in-law; for his only daughter to step down from the landed gentry to marry the son of a poor country schoolteacher must indeed be a disappointment to him.

Lady Thornhill took a chair. "You have made things very difficult for me," though she seemed not too upset. "Sir James speaks of 'nurturing a viper in his bosom,' of being ill repaid for his long friendship with you, William. He is willing to take Jane back, but vows that he never wishes to set eyes on William again. Perhaps if you were to return, Jane, you could make peace with your father, and William would then be accepted."

Jane leaped to her feet. "Mother! How can you even suggest such a thing! Billy is my lawful husband, and I am his wife. If that is Father's last word, then he has lost a daughter; a daughter who has always been dutiful, and loved him dearly." She was on the brink of tears.

"Pish-tush, child!" Lady Thornhill did not make the mistake of trying to soothe her daughter with endearments. "Your return would speed the matter, but I did not expect that you would listen to such reasonable advice or I would not have brought your wardrobe with me. Your father's anger is a measure of his love for you, and he has always had a high regard for William. But you must needs be patient for a while. Now show me your new home, Jane."

Mother and daughter went together to inspect the small apartment, and then into the studio to see the work that William had in progress. They discussed and agreed on a list of feminine needs, including more pots for the kitchen, and Jane's favorite mirror, which Lady Thornhill would bring with her on her next visit. Then William saw her down to her carriage and she drove off.

William could see that Jane was happy enough, but was finding it a little difficult to be patient. She had always been her father's favorite, far more than her brother John, who now spent most of his time at the family estate in Dorset. More than once she railed against her hardhearted parent, and seemed to derive solace from pouring both wifely and daughterly love upon her new husband.

William Hogarth was lucky, he still had his work. That work must justify his Jenny's belief in him. It must bring to her new life the comforts and small luxuries she had renounced as Jane Thornhill to become Jane Hogarth, and it must show Lady Thornhill that she was not mistaken in her son-in-law.

Undoubtedly his work was the sole hope of clearing the breach between the two households. Sir James' judgment of Hogarth would be the judgment of one artist by another. Once William was successful and had attained some fame, Sir James would be unable to ignore him if only on artistic grounds. Anything short of this would be hardship for Jane.

Living in Lambeth was cheaper than in London, and though William had to make the trip to town several times a month, to see printers and booksellers, he found the walk a pleasant one, with much to observe along the way; two miles or so along the south bank of the river to the shabby settlements of Southwark, then over London Bridge to the City. But Lambeth had few amusements for a young woman; there were no theatres, nor could Jane find friends of her own class and background with whom to take tea, or a dish of gossip.

However there were the Vauxhall Pleasure Gardens. These lay conveniently near, to the west of Southwark, and on the south bank of the river. Almost as though to supply the Hogarths' need, the old Gardens, famous in the days of Charles II, were shortly opened under new ownership. To Hogarth's profit as well as pleasure, for the new owner, Jonathan Tyers, commissioned two oil portraits to adorn the Garden art gallery. He left the subject matter to the artist, who chose to do King Henry VIII and his wife, Ann Boleyn. Portrait painting was never to William's taste, and in this case he did little more than a sound commercial job. But he was scarcely back at his usual work when the popularity of the royal portraits brought him another order; this was to engrave silver passes as tickets of admission for visitors who had taken out a yearly subscription instead of paying at the gate. Other commissions followed and Hogarth fell into the role of artistic advisor to his friend Tyers.

The Hogarths began to prosper. But it was by hard work rather than by any such striking success as William coveted in order to close the breach between himself and Sir James. Lady Thornhill continued to pay regular and somewhat stately visits, but brought no fresh news. And his Jenny, sweet-tempered little Jenny, could still be roused to anger at any suggestion that she return to Covent Garden.

Whenever he was in town William went to visit his mother and sisters in the little shop in Long Walk. They begged his advice on every matter under the sun, from the scandalous price of tea and whether they should afford it, to the fit of a new gown Ann was fashioning for some grand lady. But never, so far as he knew, did they take his advice. He was the Male of the Family, a sort of figurehead to ornament the ship, but scarcely expected to be of any real value in the sailing of it. Once he took Jane to visit the busy sempstresses. But after that she made some excuse or other; he could guess the reason. The calm, undemanding affection between the members of the Hogarth family was too bitter a reminder of the recent breach between herself and her father.

As the second year of their marriage came to an end William was too busy to be discontented, Jane too young and vital to remain unhappy. The simple anniversary tokens were exchanged between them, and William guilefully suggested that it had been some time since Jane had been to the Vauxhall Gardens.

Jane fell in with the idea. "And you shall show me your work there, by night, when all the candles are lit." She decreed that, since this was a special occasion, the whole household must share in the jaunt: Betsey the maid, as faithful as ever, though an indifferent cook, and Dickon, a sturdy boy who ran errands, cleaned shoes and pots and pans, and tonight could carry a club and a lantern to see them safely home.

William donned his sword, his newest wig, and the red coat with its enormous patch pockets and huge silver buttons down the front. Jane put on a gay frock of green taffety, very wide over the hooped underskirt, very narrow at the waist, and perched a smart little green-ribboned straw hat over her best lace cap. William thought she looked enchanting.

Then, with Jane's hand on William's arm, preceded by Dickon proudly swinging his club and followed by Betsey, they took the road along the riverside, all singing rounds and catches like true Londoners. The rutted lane lay peaceful in the sunset, for the river was still the main highway. They reached the river stairs which gave access to the Pleasure Gardens. But what a shouting, brawling mob was there!

Surely a riot must have broken out! Coarse watermen fought, cursing, to bring their craft, loaded with pleasure-seekers, in to the splashed and muddy steps. Rough characters waiting on the shore, discharged soldiers or worse, waded into the shallows, shoving the boats away, determined to carry the passengers ashore and so extort a few pennies for their unwanted services. The hired Garden guards seemed only to add to the confusion. Women screamed, in real or pretended terror; a group of youthful revelers, gay in swords, wigs and satin waistcoats, opposed the blackmailing longshoremen with shouts and force. Their boat was overturned and they struggled, spluttering, from the water.

But this was only rowdy, good-humored London, and family parties seemed to come unscathed from the fray Armfuls of children were being set ashore, shrilling their excitement; two seeming pirates staggered beneath the massive buttocks of a tradesman's wife, while another seeming pirate ignominiously tucked her small but furious husband beneath his elbow and set them on the steps. Loud laughter, mingled with the roar of battle, came to the Hogarths' ears as they presented themselves at the entrance gate.

Jane frowned. "Oh, Billy, I had quite forgot; Mr. Tyers will not be expecting us. We come as simple pleasure-seekers who must pay our shillings. Did you remember your money?"

This was the proud moment for which William had been waiting. Carefully he searched his pockets; then again, as the crowd began to press and murmur from behind.

"Not a ha'penny," he confirmed cheerfully. "Only this," and with a grin produced a small golden plaque.

The gateman took it, raised it to the light to read what was engraved. Then in the rich boom of a toastmaster at a civic function announced, *"Mister William Hogarth, benefactor and life member of the Vauxhall Pleasure Gardens.* Pass Mister Hogarth and party!"

An amused cheer rose from the crowd behind. Jane gave a delighted squeeze to William's arm. But as he tucked the golden ticket away in safety, had to register the wifely protest. "Oh, Billy, what extravagance!"

"A token of esteem from our good friend Mister Tyers. Partly in gratitude for my past services in embellishing the Gardens, partly, I am sure in the hope that I should continue to embellish them . . . with you, my dear!" There, he had worked in the compliment that he had been hatching up all day!

"Oh, Billy darling!"

The golden entrance ticket seemed to gild the whole of the evening. Mr. Tyers was absent but an assiduous young assistant bowed low, was presented to Jane, and took charge of the party. He showed Dickon and Betsey to the servants' waiting quarters, where for a few pennies they could find refreshment and the company of other servants. Then he led the Hogarths to the Pleasaunce, an avenue of perfect trees jeweled against the darkening skies by a thousand torches and candles. And there, in the Garden proper, Mr. Tyers himself awaited them.

'Twas an occasion, and the formal ceremony did justice to it. Mr. Tyers thrust forward the hilt of his court sword, bent his left knee almost to the ground, and with an elaborate flourish laid his hat against his heart. Jane acknowledged with a graceful curtsey. William armed his hat beneath his left elbow and executed the correct bow, which however may have lacked something of Mr. Tyer's dancing-master elegance. Then they were free to chat, and to accept the offer of the owner of the Gardens to escort them through its more notable attractions.

Members of the upper classes might frequent Vauxhall for flirtation and dalliance; middle-class families to gape and admire. But to the lower classes who could pay their shillings and borrow suitable attire, the glory of the Gardens was past imagining, sheer magic. Here, by the art of the ingenious Mr. Tyers, a hard-working apprentice might be king for a night.

Along the wide paved or gravel walks, smooth as house-flooring, the owner led his honored guests. Jane, who had seen them before but only in cold daylight, exclaimed over the marvels of airy pavillions, lodges convenient in case of a shower of rain, groves, lawns, temples, grottos and sparkling cascades. Statues and paintings adorned the porticoes and embellished the vast and tasteful colonnades. 'Twas all the height of elegance.

Everywhere strolled the gayest company, perfumed and posturing; gallants and beaux with their ladies in silks and satins and laces. Many bowed acknowledgment to the famous proprietor; some, to Jane's swelling pride, greeted Hogarth the artist. In the deepening dusk the lights shone more brilliantly. Bows, curtseys, haughty or admiring glances had to be returned in kind. Now the lights shone more brilliantly in the night, sparkling like a thousand constellations. It was said that the King's own palace could not approach the lavish wealth of candle-light that ennobled Vauxhall Gardens.

Such marvels did not grow of themselves. As Mr. Tyers explained, each smallest detail had to be planned, tried and amended. And his most difficult problem was not the Gardens themselves but the people who frequented it. Every pleasure-seeker turned back at the gates reduced the profit; yet to admit all who offered their shillings might result in riotous conduct and a thousand guineas' damage on a single night. As an example, he had hoped to restore the masquerades so popular in the days of Queen Anne; only to find that, disguised behind their masks, many unsuitable people gained admittance. Nor was that the only trouble, for even those of better birth and breeding made their incognitos an excuse for unseemly behavior which would have brought the Gardens into disrepute. Two duels had been fought, but fortunately without loss of life.

Pausing briefly to allow Jane to admire William's paintings, the proprietor sought her approval of some recently added attractions. One was a damp-looking grotto or stone ruin lined with cockleshells, and actually inhabited by a staring-eyed tangle-haired hermit robed in sacking. He looked blue and chilly, poor thing. More to her liking

was an amusing conceit, a large painted scene of a mill
and miller's cottage so contrived that the millstream
could be seen actually splashing over the turning wheel
and you could hear the sound of falling water. This wondrous exhibition lasted a full fifteen minutes, then the
painted canvas had to be wound back upon its rollers and
restarted. William, as interested in stage sets as he was in
depicting action in his paintings, had to go behind the
scenes to examine the machinery.

The Rotunda, a large pleasure dome resting upon such
slender pillars that it seemed to float in the air, gave forth
the dulcet tones of fiddles and bassoon, and a performance
of the airs of Mr. Handel, who was now a resident of
London. Then Mr. Tyers begged that the Hogarths
would join him in a cold collation at one of the small
tables set up in the Rotunda itself. Perhaps a hundred such
tables were set about; at these dined family parties and
more fashionable groups of citizens. Waiters with upheld
trays glided between the crowded tables, though how they
managed it was a marvel in itself. Knives and forks and
human tongues clattered without cease. And through it
all the fiddles and bassoons murmured a pleasing under-
current to the scene of gaiety.

But poor Mr. Tyers was scarcely able to enjoy his own
creation. Like the captain of a ship, he was seldom free
from his duties. His assistants, dressed like gentlemen
but in more sober fashion, came, first one, then another
to consult him. And at last, profuse in his apologies, he

was called away; important nobility from abroad had to be met, greeted and escorted.

William beamed at his bride. She returned his smile with a sigh of sheer bliss. Above them floated the cupola, starred with lamps, airy as a veil, remote almost as the night sky . . . and far more romantical. Then she glanced down at the table.

"Billy, I'm so hungry!" she mourned. "The roast chicken was smaller than a pigeon squab, and I declare I can see the plate through this slice of ham."

William laughed. "The carver boasts that from a single ham he can carpet the whole Gardens in pink and white. For real food, give me home, or a common eating house." Then, glancing at a nearby table he gave an exclamation.

"Do you know her?" Jane asked, following his attention.

Gayly elegant, rich with jewels, a pretty girl of sixteen or so was entertaining an elderly gentleman with all the practiced airs and graces of an accomplished courtesan.

"I'm trying to think." Automatically William reached in his pocket for pencil and paper. He had left them at home, but the action stirred his memory. "A coaching yard . . . probably the Bell. Not a coach though, only a wagon. Yes, the York Wagon, but I can't be sure till I find the sketch I made!" He slapped his thigh with that somewhat common gesture Jane hoped she had broken him of. "Just a country girl, pink-cheeked and pretty in her way . . . with a goose, yes, a goose, of all things! But what a way she has come in a few short weeks, poor child!" He sounded sad.

"Lucky child, surely." Jane couldn't repress the slight envy in her voice. "How she dotes on life! And how rich she must be!"

"In a year or so she may have nothing. Worse than nothing in five years. You don't understand." He pushed back his chair. "Come, we'll seek out Betsey, and the boy to light our way home. It is late and tomorrow I have work to do."

5: The First Progress

NEXT MORNING William Hogarth was already at work when Jane came into the studio. The draft from the open window blew a number of sketches off the table. Jane picked them up, replaced them in their portfolio and weighted it down with a discarded copperplate. William went on with his work.

He owed Jenny an explanation for having abruptly put an end to their jaunt to the Vauxhall Gardens, particularly as it was their wedding anniversary. He was not very skillful with words, but perhaps his pencil would help him out.

"The sketch is lost, or given away. I am making a new one, from memory," he said.

Jane set a stool beside him, dusted off the top with a paint rag, and seated herself to watch. "Yes, it already bears a likeness to the girl in the Gardens, though from the other side of her face."

"I have trained myself to catch likenesses. I never forget a nose or a chin. The dress I am not sure of . . ." A few strokes of the lead-pointed pencil dismissed it as unimportant. "But since she has traveled down in the York Wagon she wears a countrified straw hat over a cap. But scissors?" He paused to consider. "What makes me think of scissors?"

"Because she sought employment as a sempstress, and the scissors, if she wore them, would tell people her trade," Jane contributed. "Just as carters carry a whip and maids a broom at a hiring fair. They'd hang on a ribbon from her waist."

"Of course. I see it now. And thank you." Two ovals and a few lines denoted the York Wagon. A few more, and one saw a lean man on a bony old horse. "Her father I think, re-reading a letter of introduction he has brought with him from his country parson, or perhaps a written recommendation for the girl which he is going to leave with her, now that he has seen her safely through her journey.

"Yes, safely, he thinks. He has never heard of the notorious woman who has just stepped up to his daughter, and chucking her under the chin in friendly fashion says, 'How pretty you are, my pet!' When I paint her she will be elegantly attired, with a fine lace cardinal, a dress of heavy silk, and a dozen patches on her face, more to conceal the ravages of the life she has led than for ornament. In fact Mother Needham."

It wrung a protest from tender-hearted Jane. "Oh, no, Billy. You can't put her in. Why, she's the most notorious procuress in all London."

The pencil sketched on remorselessly. "That's why I remember the scene so well. And in the background Colonel Chartres and his jackal. He'll buy the girl from Mother Needham, dress her, train her and send his pimp, John Gourlay, around to find customers for her charms. Before I start on the real picture I'll sketch Chartres and Gourlay at some coffeehouse, so I'll get a good likeness."

"Poor Billy! So that's what spoiled the evening for you and led to our hasty return?" Jane's feeling of pique had vanished.

"Nonsense!" William's tone was gruff. "I felt the need to get back to paper and pencil and test my memory. But now you know where I first saw this Molly . . . Mary, whatever she calls herself." He tossed the rough layout into Jane's lap.

The hasty sketch could mean little except to another artist, but Jane's fingers stroked it affectionately. For here was something of Billy's work that she herself had helped to fashion. Perhaps she could go on helping. "Molly? She must have a second name. Molly Hackabout? Wasn't there a Kate Hackabout hanged last month; she started as a whore, and took to thieving? And will you paint it on canvas for Mr. Tyers to show?"

William frowned. That was the worst of women. Perhaps because their own tasks were many and brief they saw a painting finished, framed, sold and hung before even the palette had been prepared. The story of Molly Hackabout . . . he must remember the name . . .

would take weeks of preparation and painting. "I'm not sure I shall paint it."

"Oh, but you must!" Jane was firm. It was her picture.

William relented. "Perhaps I'll engrave the sketch, as a warning to country girls. A thousand people scan a print for every one that examines a painting."

"But why should they take warning?" Jane protested. "It will be just a picture of a lucky girl finding employment the minute she reaches London. Country folk aren't likely to recognize Mother Needham or Colonel Chartres. They'd never have heard of them!"

Jane was exasperating, because she was right. "Then I'll do a second engraving, showing her at Vauxhall; showing what has become of her."

Jane laughed pleasantly, but only adding to William's irritation. "Billy, dear, for a married man how little you know of women! Would you warn a girl 'Be good, or someone may dress you in silks, load you with jewels and take you to Vauxhall Pleasure Gardens to dine!' "

William Hogarth threw down his pencil, rose, and on short plump legs began to pace the studio. Scared at her own temerity, Jane folded her hands in her lap to steady them and managed to smile.

William came to a halt, turned and snapped. "Well?"

"Only William Hogarth can advise William Hogarth, so I'll put your thoughts into your own words." Jane's voice was a little uneven. 'Why doesn't that pest Jenny go back to her household tasks and leave me to work in peace? If I weren't the sort of husband I am I'd take a stick to her.' All right, so far?"

William grunted.

"Good!" Jane sounded more confident. "And the next great thought is, 'Jenny doesn't know the first thing about art; but come to think of it, nor do the people who buy engravings. Could that mean that what Jenny thinks is what they think . . . that Jenny may be right after all? Of course I can't take her advice, but thinking it out independently I realize there is something in what she says. Not that she knows what she is talking about. Perhaps I could do a set of four prints as I did with *The Four Times of the Day;* only more like scenes on the stage, with the same central characters. I've often thought of writing a play with pictures.' "

A reluctant grin split William's round features. "Witches," he announced, "have no place in an artist's studio. They should tend their cauldrons."

"I'm just going," Jane rose with a flurry of skirts. "I must see that the leg of mutton is fully basted." But not quite certain of her success she still delayed.

"You go on one condition." William was first at the door and opened it gallantly. "That having added immeasurably to my future labors you will return to lighten them!"

Thenceforth the consultations took place almost daily. William Hogarth could record what he saw; few better.

He had an amazing memory for faces as he was fond of declaring, and prided himself on being a physiognomist. He could catch action, whether of a person or an object in motion, as a tea table being overthrown with its cups. But it was Jane who was called upon to describe appropriate clothes and even furnishings. And sometimes she would suggest a pose, or a grouping.

To make more of a story, Molly and her elderly keeper were removed from the Rotunda to private lodgings, small, but richly furnished, though not in the best of taste. Beyond it, a bed with canopy and from a further room emerges a little blackamoor, Toby, with silver collar and feathered turban, brings in a silver teakettle, while a small pet monkey, equally fashionable, plays on the floor with one of Molly's fine lace caps.

"Molly hasn't the sense to know when she is well off"—William explained his partly finished sketch—"so she has taken a younger lover. There he is, hiding behind the door. Give him a longish sword and he's a fencing master who ogled her acquaintance at the Gardens the night we saw her. Perhaps he picked a quarrel with the elderly protector, demanding the address under pretense of sending his seconds with a cartel for a duel. Of course they never came, but the fencing master did. And today the protector has returned home unexpectedly early. Molly seats him and pours his tea. Then creates a diversion by upsetting the tea table so that the scalding water pours upon his legs. And under cover of the confusion her maid whom we'll call Sally, hurries the new lover out to safety."

"The horrid little creature!" exclaimed Jane.

"The next sketch shows Molly, or Mary Hackabout, in Bridewell where she has been hauled off to prison. Still in the remains of her finery, with other flashy prostitutes, she is forced to beat hemp." Even the rough sketch was full of action and story and so sordid that it seemed actually to stink of the prison.

"But how did she get there?" Jane wanted to know.

"The usual way, I suppose. Once her protector began to suspect her it was easy enough to have her watched. He threw her out and if she ever had a chance of becoming a fashionable mistress it was now gone. She took whatever men she could and so sank lower and lower."

"But you must show that too," protested Jane. So Scene Three, after several sketches were made and discarded, came into being.

Mary Hackabout again takes tea. But under what different circumstances. Of course the little blackamoor and monkey have gone, but the maid Sally is still with her. The delicate furniture is replaced by a rush-bottomed chair and a clumsy stool-like table. Molly is exhibiting a man's watch, which she may have stolen. Or it may have been given her, since the wig box on the tester of her bed bears the initials of James Dalton, a highwayman who had recently been hanged at Tyburn. In the background, unseen by the two women, a magistrate and his tipstaffs enter the room, to search and arrest.

"I'll make the magistrate Sir John Gonson, who's disliked for his violent persecution of the fallen women," Hogarth decided. "People will recognize the likeness and point him out to others; that's the kind of thing that sells the prints."

Three scenes were now blocked in, in William's favorite medium of pencil and red crayon. Then to Jane's delight he stretched a canvas, and set his palette.

"I'll start with Scene Two, where Molly upsets the table. I must get down the girl we saw at the Gardens before I forget some detail of her appearance. I can use types or studies for the others," he explained, "but she is the leading actress in our tragedy. Once I have sketched what she looks like I know her character and how she will behave. That's the science of physiognomy."

"You mean if ever you painted me you would know all about me, my inmost thoughts?" Jane pouted. "Then, sir, you shall never delineate me!"

William laughed, and began to sketch in lightly the diagonal guide lines which helped him compose his picture.

A dozen times a day Jane left her household duties to note the progress of "her" story. Molly's character, as discussed between her and William, had been interesting enough, but the pencil sketch in which a line stood for a doorway and an oval for a face had meant little to her.

Now real people were beginning to emerge, and in color too. And how clever of Billy to depict those falling tea-cups in the very act of shattering on the floor. And that rich old man . . . why you could almost hear his startled curse as the scalding tea splashed on his leg!

The work went so well that William Hogarth felt it wise to return to his first scene, in the inn-yard, and make the slight changes in Molly Hackabout that turned her into the simple country girl she had so recently been. He was lucky enough to track down Colonel Chartres and his jackal at their usual coffeehouse, and hastened back to transfer them also to his canvas. Mother Needham he had seen scores of times, and even Jane thought she re-cognized the small portrait as someone she had en-countered in the streets of London.

No artist likes to have an observer breathing down his neck, but after one disappointed protest, "Oh, that isn't as I imagined it!" had been met by withering silence, Jane learned discretion. And William came to value the occasional breathless, "Yes . . . oh, yes!" as a figure grew to life. For what Jane liked, others would as well. Her father's murals were prized as the best that were being done in England, but he painted from imagination, and depicted scenes that might mean something to a classical scholar, but little or nothing to his daughter. She would never point to a Thornhill figure on the ceiling of a banqueting hall and say excitedly, "Why I saw a man just like that in the vegetable market this morning!"

Of course, as William had to admit to himself, this wasn't Art. But the engravings, once he reached that stage, seemed likely to have a popular sale, if Jane's appreciation could be taken as a sign. And once the money began to come in, William Hogarth intended to devote himself to painting after the grand manner. William Kent's blasting criticism still rankled.

He had begun on the third scene; Molly Hackabout in reduced circumstances, with evidence of her association with criminal life all about her, and the magistrate in the doorway, when Lady Thornhill, sweeping in on one of her periodical visits, invaded the studio. Jane was already there.

With a barely suppressed grunt of irritation William bade her welcome. As soon as she could extricate herself from Jane's embracing arms she walked over to examine the first two paintings. Politely he set them on chairs, to catch the best light, and explained that they were still unfinished and that he planned to make several corrections.

While Jenny praised and pointed, her mother stepped forward to examine more closely some details of brushwork, stood back again to get the general effect. William awaited her comment and braced himself to meet it politely. Unprofessional praise can be almost as disturbing as professional condemnation.

Her handsome features, socially disciplined, told nothing even to William Hogarth the physiognomist. But after a pause she said, "Come, Jane, we have news to discuss, and our chatter must not disturb your Billy."

William returned to his work, then set aside his brushes and started to sketch. For no obvious reason the interruption had given him the answer he had been seeking for the end of his drama. Imprisonment in Bridewell was not enough to serve as the warning he sought. It was not even sufficiently tragic to make a telling story, for thousands of women were sent there for minor offences. Should his character die there? No, better to show her released, resuming her sordid life, and sinking lower and lower into shame and misery.

Her death scene, in still barer lodgings, with Sally the maid scarce waiting for her mistress' last breath, but already rifling her trunk of its poor trifles. For the usual portraits which the London public delighted to identify in the prints, why not insert two well-known quack doctors, quarreling violently over what had been the cause of the death?

Gruesome enough? Not for the popular taste! There would have to be one more scene, the sixth. The body, disregarded even at the funeral feast. The coffin, open at the head and slightly distorted so as to show the face of Molly, the foot of it being used as a convenient table by the neighboring harpies who had gathered to enjoy the free food and drink. The clergyman, which also could be a portrait, is too intent on the flashy younger woman seated beside him to notice that he is spilling his glass. Set in another man behaving with equal disrespect. Make both men well-known characters; but who could be decided later.

And why not emphasize the tragedy still more by an unwanted child, a little boy? Playing with a top in this scene, but set him back into some of the earlier plates. Yes, that would increase the emphasis.

"Billy, Mother's just going."

The son-in-law returned to the present and his duties. "But surely you will stay for a few minutes?"

Lady Thornhill gave him an amused smile. "I have already been here three hours. You are as bad as my husband, who knows nothing of time, but only whether the light is good or bad for his work."

"And Mother has taken a liking to the two paintings, and wishes to borrow them," Jane burst in. "She may, mayn't she, Billy?"

What could William say? Lady Thornhill had shown her affection for him in countless ways, and her visits had done much to make Jane happy.

"But you will be careful of them in the carriage, won't you, Mother?" Jane took his agreement for granted. "Some of the paint is still soft."

Lady Thornhill sniffed delicately and exchanged an amused glance with her son-in-law. After all she had lived among artists all her married life and was quite accustomed to the tenderness with which one should treat freshly painted canvas. She called the footman, who bore away the paintings, his arms stiffly holding them clear of his coattails. Jenny set to work to persuade William to complete the set of six.

In the next few weeks he was too engrossed in his work on the story and the sketches, then on the paintings that followed, to give much thought to the missing canvases. Except to wish that he had warned Lady Thornhill not to leave them about where Sir James' glance might fall upon them. Art should glorify, not record reality. The paintings were good of their kind, so far as he could recall, perhaps the best he had done to date, but it would be absurd to compare such scenes of London with the noble scope of Thornhill's own work.

Lady Thornhill's next visit was unaccountably delayed, and Jane began to worry. So did William, but for another reason. Lady Thornhill never fell ill. Her delay, he felt sure, was for another reason. Sir James had somehow seen those two paintings; he would not need to ask where they had come from. He would certainly recognize the work of the man who had been his assistant and favorite pupil, and he had wreaked his fury against his unaccepted son-in-law upon the canvases themselves. Burned them, belike; William could almost smell the paint bubbling on the canvas.

When finally Lady Thornhill's carriage halted in the road below, William had prepared himself for the worst. For Jane's sake he would declare that he should have cautioned her mother against the effect on one artist of another's work. And that, in any case, there were many changes that he needed to make, now that he knew his subject more intimately, and that he would do better to start afresh on a clean canvas.

To show his unconcern he let Jane race down to greet her mother and, paintbrush in mouth, met them both at the top of the stairs. They were sharing a joke, as usual, and when Lady Thornhill offered her cheek to her son-in-law, all that practiced physiognomist could detect was a faint flush from the effort of climbing. Certainly no sign of contrition.

It was Jane who said suddenly, "But, Mother! The two pictures?

"You warned me, child, to be careful of them." Lady Thornhill seemed amused. "And I thought that three journeys would hardly be good for them. And besides, you will have so many other things to pack."

"Mother! You don't mean . . ." Jane's voice was joyous.

Her mother silenced her with a graceful gesture of her fan, and continued to cool herself after her exertion. "I hung the two pictures in the dining room, where the morning light best suited them. When my dear old bear had nearly finished his breakfast he caught sight of them and rose to examine them more closely. First in curiosity, then in growing interest. He did not hear when I asked if I should pour him another cup."

"And then?" The artist in William burst forth. "What did he think of them?"

Lady Thornhill chuckled. "My dear bear grunted dryly, 'A man who can furnish representations like these can also maintain a wife without a portion.' "

At any other time the grudging approval of his old friend would have counted more to William than the generous approval from another source. But there was something in Lady Thornhill's manner which had led him to expect more, far more. He could only hope that Jane had not had similar fruitless hopes.

Jane gave a little arrogant toss to her head. "I am glad that Father is artist enough to appreciate Bill's true merits."

"Pish-tush, child!" Lady Thornhill administered a sharp rebuke with her folded fan. "He wants your artist back again. So come home with me now and kiss your father. We have missed you both greatly, your father and I."

WILLIAM HOGARTH'S LONDON

6: *The Golden Head*

THERE WAS no formal reconciliation, but the warmth of Sir James' welcome to his only daughter made this unnecessary. Jane bubbled with happiness to be back in her parent's home in Covent Garden, and every facility was offered William Hogarth to carry on with his work. In a way it was a homecoming for him as well, for he was soon established in a corner of Thornhill's big studio behind the house, where he had worked so often in earlier days.

Nothing could be more unlike Sir James' large, grandiose murals than his son-in-law's delicate and detailed engravings. To speed production William engaged the services of an assistant who had worked with him before, but halfway through the first engraving the man fell ill. Hogarth was obliged to carry on, though he found the work tedious and far too close a reminder of his apprentice days. Sir James was fascinated by the exacting craft of copperplate engraving; he even tried his own hand at the burin; as pleased as an old dog at learning a new trick.

These were halcyon days for William. The contented, almost luxurious surroundings left him free, as few artists ever are, to devote himself entirely to his work, and in between to spend long hours wandering the streets of his beloved London. No two parts of the city were alike; it was truly a series of villages that had been linked by crafts and commerce, and was slowly melding into a whole. Yet each kept its special quality, around the village green, or a great estate house, or the church, or some similar center. Covent Garden as well had a strong flavor and personality of its own.

Within Hogarth's own memory the Garden had been a green square surrounded by the mansions of the nobility. Now it was a graveled quadrangle in which congregated market women selling flowers, fruit and vegetables, sellers of quack medicines, and a host of raffish, seedy adventurers. While all around had sprung up shops, and the taverns and coffeehouses which had become the haunts of writers, pamphleteers, actors, and even a few painters, such as Hogarth. Sometimes the Square itself would be invaded by a riotous mob of 'prentices swarming in to play football, or by the bawds, criminals, pimps and beggars from the filthy narrow alleys that branched off from all sides. It was a wonderful place for Hogarth to sketch his subjects, he had only to step out of his own front door and there was a sample of London all around him, coarse, lusty, criminal or industrious, pulsating with excitement. What more could an artist ask for?

Eagerly as he explored the neighborhoods, Hogarth returned as conscientiously to the Thornhill studio, though he tended to dismiss his engraving as a craft, something less than an art. Since he was also becoming an excellent businessman, he planned to advertise the new plates in *The Country Journal,* at a guinea for the set of six. He discussed this with Jane and decided to charge a half guinea for the subscription. The receipt for this included a small engraving to add to its attractiveness, and the number of these advance subscriptions would let him know well ahead of time how many prints should be struck off. The advertising and publicity brought prospective buyers to the studio in a surprising number.

They came, they paid, they returned to watch the process of the pictures being transferred to the copperplate and to marvel at the strange fashion in which they came out in the black-and-white proofs, always of course in reverse of the painting itself. Already, long before the first prints were scheduled for publication, twelve hundred sets had been subscribed for.

But the constant rap on the door knocker, the unceasing influx of visitors began to irk Sir James, who was no longer young. His murals might fill a church with sightseers, but they had always left his workshop professionally peaceful.

It was Jane, on an early morning visit to the studio, who brought matters to a head. She came in, fresh as a rose in her lace cap and white apron over the full-skirted woolen housedress, and glanced around. "Father hasn't come yet?" she asked in a half whisper.

William glanced up from the delicate task of engraving the face of the dying Molly Hackabout. He shook his head. No, and come to think of it Sir James' visits to his own studio had become rarer and rarer.

But Jane had her own problem. "It's Mother, Billy." She was suddenly almost in tears. "She can't seem to realize that I'm no longer just a daughter in the house. She lets me do this, and lets me do that. But I'm not really responsible for anything. I can't even give an order to the servants, not even to my own Betsey, without her checking on it. She wants all orders to go through her. I'm a married woman now, Billy . . ."

William smiled. "So, I believe, is your mother."

Jane swallowed her tears to give a watery smile. "Mm. I hadn't thought of that. But that makes it all the more reason . . . couldn't we . . ." she came out with a rush, "couldn't we have a home of our own again?"

William laid down his tool to consider the matter. "There's plenty of money coming in," he agreed slowly. "I don't want to hurt your father's feelings by seeming ungracious . . ."

"I don't think he'd be hurt. We could find a house nearby, nearer than Lambeth."

It was a good idea, and William was beginning to wonder if Sir James wouldn't even be a little relieved.

When the afternoon light began to fade he carried the problem with him to the Bedford Arms, one of the more than four hundred of London's taverns and coffeehouses which were the meeting places of politicians, wits and merchants engaged in foreign trade, with a sprinkling of artists and writers.

A buzz of wholly masculine conversation greeted him as he entered. The rich aroma of coffee beans roasting in the back premises and the thick whorls of tobacco smoke which hung in the still air guarded such places against the danger of female intrusion. He exchanged a few jests and greetings, found a seat, and an attendant brought him his usual cup of coffee. He was still stirring in the rich dark demerara sugar when in walked John Thornhill, still in his traveling clothes, and threw his heavy roquelaure cape on a hook.

"Just up from the country." John clapped his brother-in-law on the shoulder in greeting. "Thought I might meet you here and catch up on the news before reporting to the parents. How do they fare?"

William told him, and that led to Jane's restlessness and her desire for a home of her own.

"Hardly blame her," John Thornhill agreed. "I adore my mother. But . . . and by that but I mean when I was young I used sometimes to break an ornament just to get beaten and relieve the strain. Nowadays I arrange for my factor to send word of some crisis on the estate which demands my immediate return to Dorset." He set down his cup of steaming chocolate as an idea struck him. "Why don't you and Jane come and live with me, down in the country? There's room for a whole family, if Jane's thoughts run that way."

The genuine warmth of the invitation, and the absurdity of ever leaving London had a double charm for William. In the studio a dozen sketches, paintings and engravings in various stages awaited completion; he must be close to his printer, and near to his models and their city background of streets and alleys. He was helping Sir James with cartoons on his next murals, and even assisting in a small way in instructing the Thornhill art classes. Impossible? Of course it was!

John mistook his silence for indecision. "Sam!" He beckoned a mutual friend, a landscape painter, Samuel Scott, to join them. "Tell William about cows standing in pellucid streams, and golden fields of barley bending in the breeze, and all the other things you paint. And don't forget sunsets. I'll wager William has never seen a sunset untinged by London smoke. He must come to Dorset."

"William has not yet lived." Solemnly Scott inclined his bewigged head. "Yet to tear his roots from London would surely cause his death. All his life he has breathed naught but smoke and if he belched he would emit black sulphurous fumes like a cannon. In fresh air he would expire like a fish out of its natural element."

"True enough!" William Tothill, a draper, turned from a neighboring table to join in the conversation. "Yet if small doses of air were prescribed to our patient at first . . ."

Thornhill slapped the table. "Tothill is right. The first step is to acclimatize our valued William, and"—he included Tothill and Scott in his glance—"will you not join us?" he invited. "So desperate a London character requires a strong guard, otherwise we would scarce drag him as far as London Bridge."

Hogarth suppressed a grin. He had no clear idea of what was intended but he had scarce had a day's holiday since he was his own master. And perhaps the real countryside would furnish him with fresh ideas for pencil and brush. He decided to surprise his mocking friends.

"Very well. When do we start? Where do we go?"

The effect was all that he had hoped. Tothill stared, Scott almost dropped his cup. Even John Thornhill was taken aback; but he had much of his mother's strength of purpose.

"Tomorrow?" he asked slowly.

"It's a clear night." Hogarth pressed his point. "Why not right now?"

So began the childish escapade of five very respectable London gentlemen. For before they left the coffeehouse

Ebenezer Forest, a lawyer with literary bent, had added himself to the company. Each lived near by, each returned home briefly to leave word of his planned absence and pick up a clean shirt, and, in the case of Scott an overcoat, for he dreaded the chill night air.

Singing lustily they made their way down the streets and alleys toward Billingsgate, reminding Hogarth of earlier carefree expeditions with his fellow apprentices. At Billingsgate, at Puddle Dock while awaiting the ferry across the river, Hogarth sketched a porter who went by the amusing name of the Duke of Puddle Dock.

In gusty wind and rain squalls which had suddenly blown up they sailed for Gravesend, still singing doughtily all the way; and there, at dawn, having breakfasted off biscuit, beef and neat gin, they rambled through Kent, singing, jesting, playing ridiculous tricks on one another and eating and drinking whatever came their way. Sometimes they were soaked through with the showers, they were always dirty. But for five glorious days they cast aside all middle-class decorum. When they returned to the city they recorded their hilarious holiday in a small book of verses and sketches.

Hogarth, though he had vastly enjoyed the "peregrination" had only been convinced that he was still a Londoner. He had no leaning toward becoming a country gentleman. Besides, in the field of art there was no sale for landscapes; country gentlemen were not interested in paying money for scenes which they could view every day from their own windows.

So William and Jane went house-hunting, though a little secretively at first, to avoid hurting Thornhill's feelings. Then they discovered that Jane's father and mother were in full sympathy with the plan. It was Lady Thornhill as much as Jane who discovered the small pretty house so conveniently close to Leicester Fields. It was a straight up-and-down town house, with three stories; the front door opened directly on the sidewalk, with the kitchen and pantry in the basement, and attics for the servants above. They would need more servants to run such an establishment, but now they could afford them. Betsey would accompany Jane from the Thornhill house as she had once gone with her mistress to Lambeth. Once established, Hogarth settled into the new studio with a sigh of relief, to finish his engravings.

The first of the sets was to be delivered from the printers in the autumn of 1734. Two days before the delivery date Hogarth was taking coffee in the Bedford Arms when one of his subscribers came across to his table, waving a print in his face. "If you let other engravers copy your work before the date of issue," he accused, "your subscribed prints will be stale and valueless."

Hogarth snatched the reproduction. It was smudgy and wretchedly done from a grotesque engraving of his *Progress,* so bad that it couldn't have been just copied from his own plate with the connivance of his printer. Indeed several details were quite wrong. Undoubtedly the engraver had done it from a close examination of the original painting in his studio, but had forgotten some of the essentials of the original.

While Hogarth was fuming over this, Tothill came in with a second print. This had been done by another engraver, that was clear, though from the same second scene of the *Progress*. It held even more mistakes. Could it have been engraved from a mere description?

His anger grew with his dismay. But he felt helpless before the problem. It was necessary for him to exhibit his paintings, since to do so often persuaded people to purchase the prints of them. But it was impossible to limit visitors to his workshop to his friends alone, or even to friends of friends. How could he prevent such plagiarism?

It was Ebenezer Forrest who made the suggestion. "This is really a form of fraud or misrepresentation of value, and should be covered by the same type of law that protects the work of an author. Queen Anne's law of copyright was passed by Parliament in 1702, but that law does not cover the work of an artist. It certainly should."

Hogarth frowned, trying to understand. If anyone had stolen one of his copperplates, then, since the mere metal represented more than a shilling, the thief could be hanged. But a painting was an idea, and ideas had no cash value. Who ever heard of stealing an idea?

But Forrest, a lawyer himself, was quite serious. He called for pen and paper, and began to discuss the problem with other friends in the room. For instance, how long should such a law limit the copying of a print? Hogarth suggested that it should be during the lifetime of the engraver or artist. Huggins, the judge, thought that it should be for a term of twenty years. Hogarth went home to talk over this worrisome new problem with Jane, who was always so level-headed.

It was a difficult problem. There were scores of copies of almost every painting of the Great Masters of the Italian school. Some were passed off as original works of the Masters themselves, but others were honest reproductions, by students or lesser artists, designed for such buyers as could not afford the price of an original. Plays too were copied, rewritten, altered; they always had been, ever since the days of Shakespeare. No Parliament, Hogarth felt, would trouble to protect the rights of a simple engraver when even the work of the great Michael Angelo could be copied by the hundred.

But the Italian painter was dead. If the right to copy could be limited to the painter's lifetime, or to a generation, say fifteen years, such a law might be passed.

For many evenings in the coffeehouse the sounds of argument raged. Then the agreed bill became a compro-

mise, limiting the right to fourteen years. That seemed
to Hogarth good enough, for in even five years, he
thought the public could have lost interest, and the
pirate engravers their hope of profit.

The copyright act was not passed in time to protect
The Harlot's Progress from innumerable imitators. No
less than eight spurious sets came on the market at a
price lower than Hogarth's. Hogarth himself issued two
other sets in a smaller size. But the quality of his work
was such as to make his own sets unrivaled, and the
profits poured in. The noted Theophilus Cibber based a
pantomime, and a ballad opera somewhat on the order of
The Beggar's Opera, on Hogarth's simple story, and
songwriters further spread its fame by making tunes for
this. Molly Hackabout's visage appeared on fans, on tea-
cups, and in all sorts of unlikely places. And though
Hogarth fumed at this cheapening of his main character,
the resulting publicity brought him from fifty to a hundred pounds weekly in further subscriptions and sales.

Jane's wardrobe reflected the generous marriage portion
that, since the reconciliation, had been accorded her by
Sir James; the fine furnishings of the new house in Leicester Fields reflected the boom in sales of *The Harlot's
Progress.* William still worked in his paint-stained gown
and turban, but thanks to Jane's quiet insistence it was
outwardly a new William who walked abroad, or paid
one of his periodic visits to his sisters' little millinery

shop in Long Walk. The stocky, short-legged figure wore a larger, whiter wig, a coat with longer, more fashionable skirt, from which protruded the newly gilded hilt of his small modish sword. But deep in the big pockets of the ornate coat lay the ever-ready pencil and sketch book. London still owned him, and as an artist he now owned London, with all its lusty cruelty, rowdy humor and stench of packed humanity, which only he could truly record and interpret.

He observed it with the dispassionate interest of his profession. In his apprentice days he had faithfully noted down the pained grimace of a man hit on the head by a pewter pot. Now he committed to memory or to paper the dread processions that formed outside the prison of a Monday morning on their way to a Tyburn hanging, and the macabre disputes between felons as to which should have the honor of being hanged first. At one time highwaymen took pride of place, but recently mail-robbers had made a good claim for precedence. Doomed men were allowed a white cap with black ribbons, and a nosegay or a sweet-smelling orange to sniff at, as they made a last speech, boasting their crimes or pleading their innocence. Below them the crowd milled, cheering, cursing or weeping, but vastly entertained. For crime, the prisons and the madhouse at Bedlam were almost the sole amusements of the very poor. And such drama was free to anyone who cared to join the shoving, yelling mob.

To the artist it was the truth that mattered, not whether the custom was good or bad. And some day, Hogarth vowed, he would picture every facet of it, on canvas or on paper. For he alone could do it.

Undeterred by the danger of contracting the deadly jail fever, he visited the madhouse at Bedlam and the prison at Newgate, intent on his favorite subject of physiognomy, the science that seeks to determine a man's nature by the study of his features. But he found that crime sprang from far too many causes for the true criminal to be determined by his looks. And when he painted Sarah Malcolm in her cell, the famous murderer awaiting execution, he was able to portray only a firm-featured woman of middle age, whom anyone might have employed as a house servant. Nonetheless the prints of the picture had a wide popular sale, at a shilling each.

Hogarth knew that if he had remained with his first craft he would by now have been at least a minor officer of the Guild of Silversmiths. His duties would have been with the night watch, with the election of sheriffs, and the mustering of city bands. As an artist his civic duties were light, only what he chose, but as an artist he could portray and draw attention to the many evils and abuses which no one had so far thought to remedy. For instance the appalling yearly increase in the number and size of painted boards and carvings that denoted inns and taverns and shops. Once such pictorial signboards were so rare as to be of value, and for lack of street names a man would

1. William Hogarth about 1732
from the Bust by François Roubiliac

2. Detail of Breakfast Scene
from Marriage-à-la-Mode

3. Hogarth's Six Servants

Study of a Girl's Head

4. Toilette Scene
   from Marriage-à-la-Mode

5. The Industrious 'Prentice at Church
from Industry and Idleness

6. The Idle 'Prentice Betrayed
from Industry and Idleness

7. He Is Surrounded by Artists and Professors
from The Rake's Progress

8. He Is Arrested for Debt
from The Rake's Progress

9. He Marries an Old Maid
from The Rake's Progress

10. Taste in High Life

11. Beer Street

12. Scene from Act 3 of The Beggar's Opera

13. David Garrick and Mrs. Garrick 1757

14. Portrait of Mrs. Hogarth

15. The Inn Yard
from The Harlot's Progress

16. The Enraged Musician

give his address as near the Sign of the Black Bear or opposite the Sign of the Golden Cock.

But nowadays there might be a dozen True Britons or Generous Britons. There was The Old English Gentleman and The Three Jolly Sailors with their portraits on the sign, and below a jingle, Coil your ropes and anchor here. Till better weather doth appear. La Belle Sauvage had been named for an Indian maid, one Pocahontas, brought from the American colonies more than a century ago, and the tavern known as The Silent Woman ironically displayed a husky farm wench with her indignant staring head clasped beneath her arm.

Each such display tried to outdo its competitors in size and elaboration. In some streets vast wooden arches spanned the narrow passageway, painted shuttlecocks rose twelve feet in the air, and gay painted wooden feathers towered to the third story of the houses. Though this battle of the signboards was not confined to London —Paris complained of similar conditions—such bulky constructions made the crowded thoroughfares still more congested by day, and at night offered convenient lurking places for footpads. Storms sometimes tore down the rotted wooden supports, or even, by sheer weight, demolished the house walls to which they were attached. They were often a serious danger to pedestrians. In 1718 a whole housefront collapsed under the burden of such a sign in Brides Lane, killing "two young ladies, the King's jeweler and a cobbler."

With his growing success William Hogarth was developing a social conscience. His pencil no longer merely recorded, it often commented, increasingly and sharply, as in his *Battle of the Signs*. Yet he was still no reformer. He indicated a need, or pointed a moral, but he did not agitate or preach . . . that was not the artist's métier.

Freed from the need to turn everything to profit, though he showed remarkable business ability in finding fresh means to sell his wares, Hogarth began to amuse himself. Among such jesting sketches he made a collection of various types of wigs. These fascinated him; those huge haystacks of white, gray or black horsehair perched atop men's shaven heads. By adjusting the angle of the wig you could greatly alter or enhance the expression of the face beneath it, portraying perturbation, anguish, and various stages of drunkenness.

Then, sensitive of his own blunt-tipped pug nose, he made a collection of all types of beaks, both normal and outlandish. Such drawings were not caricatures, but in this free exaggeration of his pencil he found some release from the exacting accuracy of his engraving tool. And for further release, when he had settled in the new house, he and Sir James began to embellish the dining room and stairway with a fine decoration of murals.

But in May of 1732 Sir James fell ill, and died peacefully in his bed. Lady Thornhill, urged by John to join him in the Dorset home, decided against such a move; she would remain in Covent Garden where she would be near Jane. In the next year William lost his mother. This left Hogarth as the sole male advisor of three households; his sisters', his own and Lady Thornhill's.

The carefree apprentice, the struggling young artist had become, whether he wished it or not, a responsible worthy citizen.

7: Tom Rakehell

ALL HIS life Hogarth retained his admiration for the grandiose murals of Thornhill, and his own desire to emulate them. Also such work had a scope and sweep far removed from the exacting detail of engraving on copperplate and was a relief from such finicky labor. So on the great staircase of St. Bartholomew's Hospital he depicted two religious incidents, The *Pool of Bethesda* and the *Parable of the Good Samaritan,* with imposing figures seven feet high, and all the crowded elaboration traditional for such works.

These works were a labor of love, but they had a double purpose. They were a generous gift to the Hospital; and Hogarth hoped that they would lead to further commissions for what he termed "historical" pictures. This hope was not realized. He had already made a reputation as a painter of portraits and with his engravings along quite another line. For him to branch out on still a third road was too difficult; his image as a particular type of artist was already fixed in the mind of his public.

So back he went to his standby, the painting of portraits, for which there was a steady demand. To vary the monotony of painting merely "kit-kats," that is head and bust down to the waist, he turned many of these commissions into "conversation pieces," a type of portraiture already well established in France, that is a family group engaged in talking together, or in some everyday amusement, such as dancing, or playing a game. But these action portraits did not wholly satisfy the nephew of Auld Hoggard, the rural story-teller. He wanted to produce another pictorial play, such as *The Harlot's Progress*, in successive scenes. Surprisingly enough such work had already paid off better than single canvases, such as portraits; the sale of the prints had proved that. And Hogarth was a sound north country businessman.

Jane had suggestions to offer. "Try this time to shun the sordid low life, Billy. Show us what happens to the rich and noble. Surely people will find that more attractive; I know I would."

A rebel duke whose head had adorned Traitor's Gate? A great landowner who had gambled away his estate and died in a duel? In desperation William even considered the tale of the Prodigal Son . . . but that had already been painted too often. Then why not a modern version of something similar, happening right here in London? Say a young man who goes from riches to rags, but who lacks the forgiving father of the biblical story? Hogarth seized paper and pencil, for an artist thinks better through the tools of his trade. And so began *The Rake's Progress*.

The boy's father dies, leaving him a large fortune in cash not in landed estate, which would carry many responsibilities. A miser's son . . . why not? That would mean a greater temptation, as the boy would have had no experience of handling money. Naturally it goes to Tom's head, and even as the will is being read his first thought is how to spend it. Have him jilt a weeping girl to show his selfishness.

The next scene almost drew itself. Young Rakehell is surrounded with the usual sycophants, bruisers, dancing masters, a fencing master, a horse jockey, and even a musician . . . and what a chance here to depict well-known characters; Hogarth had a special detestation for music and musicians. This would be staged against the background of an elegant apartment.

In Plate Three Tom Rakehell has reached a further downward step in dissipation. He is in a bawdy house, surrounded by ten or more women. He is very drunk, and his pocket is being picked by one of the molls.

Between his portraits and the paintings for the new series, William's days were filled to the brim. He rose at dawn, too early for the cook to be in the kitchen, but her small sister, Abigail, brought him a mug of small beer and buttered bread from a fresh loaf. Leaving Jane still half asleep in the big heavily curtained bed, he dressed informally, in gown and turban and strolled out to take the air in Leicester Fields. It was too early to encounter the usual beaus who rose to ride before noon, but a couple of late revelers, much the worse for wear, were slinking home like alley cats. A good subject for his pencil; anything might come in useful. The trick was to memorize what you saw and then, or later, set it down on paper.

Refreshed by the walk, he returned directly to his studio. Every hour of daylight was worth a golden guinea to a busy successful artist. He could hear Jane's voice below, setting the household to work and giving each of the servants their special orders for the day.

Now, in a becoming sacque and mob cap, she put her head in to announce that she was off for the morning's shopping, before the best in the market was already picked over.

How lucky that they lived so close to the Covent Garden market, for now there was a household of seven to provision, five servants beside the two Hogarths. They were symbolic of success and of William's relentless industry, though of course Jane's marriage portion had helped as well. There was Abigail the little maid, her older sister who ruled the kitchen, Tom the outdoor man who brought in water from the pump down the street, helped with the fires, delivered William's plates to the printers and did other odd jobs about the place, Betsey, Jane's own personal maid who mended, sewed and pressed, and Hal, the knife boy, turnspit and scullion. The maids in the Hogarth household were well paid at four pounds a year, one new outfit at Michaelmas and of course their food. Some maids were paid as much as five pounds a year now, but William thought that overex-travagant. The knife boy was clothed and fed but was not paid, and was rather like an apprentice being trained to take over a better job later in a bigger household.

Jane whisked out of the front door of the Golden Head, followed by Abigail with the shopping basket; a rather remarkable door surmounted by William's ingenious head of Van Dyke, which he had fashioned of gilded cork. Jane blew it a kiss. This was their home and she loved it.

Nearing the market they encountered their counter-parts, other mistresses with other maids, but all in similar plain wool frocks, all neatly capped, kerchiefed and aproned. Even before they reached the market the peace of the morning was shattered by forestallers shouting their wares: "Buy, buy, buy!" "Look down, look down!" . . . the milkmaid's call. "Strawberries, strawberries, who'll buy my sweet strawberries!" "Cra. .a. .abs, fish, alive oh!" though by their appearance they had been dead for a week. Jane sniffed and passed on. For fish it was safer to send Tom at four o' the morning down to Billingsgate where the catch was landed, a rough quarter of town where a lady could not go by herself.

A small herd of sheep on the way to the Smithfield butchers disputed the way with a gaggle of hissing geese, their feet tarred to save the tender webs on the long, cross-country journey from their home farm. Jane stepped from their path; city-born she was always a little afraid of their hissing heads and snake-like necks. She paused to give an order to the milk woman who regularly delivered to the Golden Head, and quite properly complained of the blueness of the milk of late. She bargained keenly for every purchase since that was expected of a thrifty housewife and there were no fixed prices, though the cost of tu'pence a pound for beef and of thr'pence a pound for mutton, so scandalous dear, could seldom be driven down. She also kept a watchful eye on the yardarm scales. There was a well-known jingle of advice to servants, *Come when you're called; do as you're bid. Shut the door after you, never be chid.* But there were just as many unspoken ones for mistresses, and one was undoubtedly *Cheapen the sales. And watch the scales.* If you didn't, you lost the respect of your servants.

It was pleasant, now that spring had come, to be able to purchase little flat nosegays of primroses, sweetly smelling of the fields, and branches of rosy may to bring into the house. As she turned homeward, followed by Abigail with the heavily laden basket, two Netherland girls in their fantastic native garb called loudly, "Buy a broom! Buy a broom!" As sure a sign of spring as the birdsongs, since they always crossed the Channel this time of year to peddle their excellent homemade brooms. "Fritters, fresh fritters!" bawled another peddler, and "New brooms for old shoes," shouted a third. And oh, wonderful, there were fresh cherries, at sixpence the pound. William would love them. But that was the last that could be crowded into the market basket.

Racing through the streets came a barber, followed by his 'prentice boy with razors and hot water and his half-moon-shaped shaving bowl. On Sunday he would be busier still, for then he would bring around to his clients their best wigs, which he had been curling during the week. It was really time that William purchased a new one, though in his studio he preferred to wear his brigand-like turban. The shaving of heads was a cleanly practice, but something was needed to protect a bare head in that cold top-floor workroom of his. And that reminded her, she must really see that he didn't get into the habit of keeping on his best coat when he started to paint, since the stray colors were so hard to remove from the cloth.

Into the big front door of the Golden Head again, and down to the stone-flagged basement kitchen, to listen to the cook's cheerful complaints regarding the purchases. When such criticisms became too tiresome Jane usually checked them by saying that next time Cook herself would have to do the early-morning marketing.

This was a pleasant place in the cool morning, with its coal-burning fireplace, its oven already warming up for the pastries, its red-sandstone sink, and the big copper to heat water on laundry days. She noted that the walls, so recently whitewashed, were already smoking up again; that was inevitable with London's soft coal. The boy, Hal, was getting the sharp edge of the cook's tongue as he turned the joint of spring lamb to roast evenly on the spit. But that was what a boy expected, and it did him no harm. William, quite rightly, refused to have one of those inhuman treadmills inside the fireplace which was turned by a miserable dog with scorched fur.

She ran lightly upstairs, two flights, to her bedroom, changed into another frock and a fresh lace cap, and caught up a long cloak.

"Come, Betsey," she called to her own maid. "I'm going round to Mother's." Betsey was always glad to leave her household mending.

Mother had now recovered from Father's death, but nothing could persuade her to go and live in John's Dorset home. She was accustomed to London, and all her friends were near by.

Over a cup of morning tea she related her latest gossip, picked up at the card tables last evening, for all fashionable London played cards almost every night of the week. Jane had news of William's last venture to relate; Lady Thornhill, who had lived most of her life among artists, took a keen and intelligent interest in her son-in-law's work. Jane could report that the prints of *Southwark Fair* were selling well, and so was *Modern Midnight Conversation,* the prints of which brought the high price of five shillings each. Jane disliked the picture; its popular sale was probably due to the many caricatured portraits of famous men in it, all very much under the influence of drink.

At the Golden Head the midafternoon dinner, the

main meal of the day, was delayed as it was so often. It was always difficult to draw William from his studio while the light was still good for working. A pleasant place, the dining room, with its reddish marble fireplace, and opening off the hallway with the wide stair. At the top of this William had painted figures behind a baluster, standing, gazing down, chatting, or strolling back into the distance. The painted scene included a modish black servant in a turban, marble pillars in noble perspective, and far off a blue sky, sunny and warm and unknown to London. Jane never wearied of looking at it, and William usually gave it a pleased glance as he came in at the door.

In the dining room the small circular table was draped with a white cloth that touched the floor; this was covered by many small dishes, since meats and pastries were all served together. William approved the cherries, but like many men, he scorned the fresh peas.

Today he was full of his plans for the final scene in *A Rake's Progress*. He would make eight plates, two more than for the former series; this would justify his increasing the price to two guineas the set. In Plate Four Tom Rakehell would be arrested for debt as he emerged from his sedan chair. The pretty girl he had heartlessly jilted in the first scene, now a sempstress, would come to his rescue with her small earnings. But in the next picture Tom is cynically being wedded to an old crippled hag, presumably for her money. And so on, to his final scene of ruin, when after much gambling and debtor's prison, he ends in Bedlam, the famous madhouse.

Hogarth told her that he intended to take a suggestion from the pirated editions of his earlier series; some of these had carried little descriptive verses. Then, catching Jane's eye, he grinned. "There is no harm in stealing from thieves," he declared.

As they rose from the table Jane suggested hopefully. "Shall you find leisure for the theatre tonight? The new play at the Drury Lane seems to be well received."

Next to his painting William preferred playgoing to any other occupation. But he shook his head. He must go to St. Martin's Lane, for this evening the pupils assembled to work from the model. With the death of Sir James, William had inherited the art school behind the Covent Garden house. This he had lately moved, with easels and model stand, from the old place to a newer and larger studio. And he planned another change.

"I have a proposal I wish to put to the class this evening," he told Jane. "Your father's idea of a free art school was excellent, but of late it has begun to attract too many idlers. The payment of a fee will reduce the numbers, and allow more individual help to be given those with real talent."

While he had been at dinner the skies had clouded; already there was a patter of raindrops in the street; men and women were hurrying home lest the drizzle turn into a real shower. Hogarth's pace was a brisk one, but he decided to turn aside a moment toward the Sign of the Unicorn, where his prints were often displayed. It was wise to check up on the printer's work from time to time, for a careless apprentice might overink the plates, or use too little, thus smudging or dimming the print. He'd cross over and see what was in the window.

But a small group, gathering despite the rain, to laugh and peer in through the square-paned window, and slap each other on the back, drew his attention. Hogarth's shortness was a disadvantage here, but for an instant, between the spectators, he could recognize what had just been put on display. The final plate of the story of Mary Hackabout. He had felt it wise to hold back the sale to the public until all the subscribed orders had been filled, so that to these viewers the picture was a new one.

The gentry had generously approved the series, now he could discover what the man in the street felt about it.

". . . And the body's scarce cold, poor creature!" exclaimed a beshawled women, shifting her empty fish basket on one ample hip.

"That there's Mother Bentley, so 'tis for sure," cackled an old man in a carpenter's square hat, delighted to have identified the notorious bawd.

And another, more decently garbed, his hand on the door and about to enter to make a purchase was saying, "By gad, I must own that picture of Elizabeth Adams.

When she ends up at Tyburn Tree I'll have summat to remember the hanging by."

"And there's the Chaplain of the Fleet Prison." A one-eyed begger identified an old professional acquaintance.

William, though unrecognized, passed happily on, his stride a bit more jaunty, his sword at a more rakish angle. Soon all London would be acclaiming the new prints, and it would not be long before he himself would be as public a figure as the imaginary creatures, such as Mary and Tom, to whom he was giving immortality.

8: Captain Coram

THE COFFEESHOPS nowadays served Hogarth as had the alehouses back in his 'prentice days. They were not only a neighborhood meeting place, they allowed birds of a feather to flock together; wits who needed to sharpen their repartee on fellow wits, merchants to exchange news of the import and export trade, artists, poets and writers to chat about their own work and gossip about one anothers', and the idlers to take their turn in reading the daily or weekly newssheets supplied by the proprietor.

One of Hogarth's favorite haunts was the Cocoa Tree; another was the Rose, next door to the Drury Lane theatre in Covent Garden and conveniently close to home. The latter was also the resort of the playactors, which gave it an added value in Hogarth's stagestruck eyes.

A coffeehouse had a way of changing character with the time of day. In the morning shipowners and their like did business there, in the afternoon pamphleteers and politicians might be found catching up with the current news and gossip. At evening it might be the meeting place of friends, and a series of self-styled philosophers could usually be heard holding forth to a select audience. From then on it deteriorated and from midnight until dawn even the Rose became notorious for the behavior of its male and female company.

The winter's day had closed in early, leaving William Hogarth too poor a light to continue work in his chilly studio in the Golden Head. But as he stepped down from the street into the Rose, the warm candlelight greeted him, and the rich odor of coffee added further welcome. A pleasant buzz of talk, with none of the acrimony which was liable to develop later in the evening, told him that he had timed his visit well.

He kicked the snow off his shoes on the stone flags, gave his heavy black roquelaure cloak a shake and hung it on a peg, then walked over to his customary seat. Wooden partitions thrust out from the wall enclosed small booths where three or four friends could form a pleasant party, or where, lacking such company, Hogarth could produce his paper and pencil without attracting too much attention.

Over by the big stone fireplace with its basket of glowing coals, a small, loudmouthed man held forth on the need to bar all foreign merchantmen from the Thames. He was always demanding an Act of Parliament. Hogarth smiled. That meant it was a Tuesday and between four and five of the clock. Now another took his place, who with almost religious zeal stammered forth his belief that if gold and silver could be abolished

Englishmen would become innocent children of nature again, like the American redskins. And after him would come the dictionary maker . . . no, he came on a Thursday . . . tonight it would be the poet.

There was none here worth sketching whom he hadn't already recorded. But here came someone whom he had been hoping to meet. A large, strongly built man, without wig or powder on his thick white locks, his weathered face reddened by the chill outdoors. Casually he slapped his hat against a massive knee and strode across to Hogarth's booth. Hogarth half rose to greet him.

"Give you good day, Coram. Hoping you would come."

"Day to you, Hogarth. Trusted to find you here as usual." Captain Coram gave a nod back toward the orator at the fireplace. "Fellow there has never seen a burned homestead, with the woman and her children butchered by the redskins, nor a man who has been tortured and scalped. There's good in them and bad in them, just the same as in Londoners. But 'innocent children of nature!' " He gave a bark of laughter. "Coffee or chocolate for you?"

Hogarth gave his order, and as the settle creaked beneath the weight of his massive friend decided once again that he must find time to paint a portrait of this remarkable man. If there were any truth in the science of physiognomy, then a picture of Captain Coram would be a history in itself, of a boy born of a seafaring family in Lyme Regis, Dorset, who had helped to sail ships as later he had helped build them, before Hogarth was born. At the time Hogarth was a 'prentice Thomas Coram, seeking wider horizons for his energy and ability, had crossed the Atlantic to the Colony of Massachusetts, and had established himself as a master shipbuilder at Taunton. But even the shipyard was too narrow a berth for this man; so, as captain of one of his own ships, he had made extensive voyages up and down the seaboard of the Colonies and back again across the Atlantic.

His broad deep skull and well-muscled frame, the powerful, thick-veined hand with which he now proffered Hogarth a pinch of rappee from a snuffbox made of West Indian tortoiseshell, all indicated the man's unusual natural resources. But where, in the face itself, could an artist find the clues to his achievements? Eyes far apart, and, in his late sixties, youthfully clear and undimmed by dissipation. A good nose, but none of those thrusting beaks that denoted ruthless ambition. A large, genial mouth, not one of those rat-traps that denoted meanness and intensity of selfish purpose.

The Captain, returning to London in his middle years, had found that his trading interests led him to a new career, and he had become a prosperous merchant. And something more besides. For when the philanthropical General Oglethorpe planned his plantations in Georgia, where persecuted Protestants from the Continent and worthy but indigent English families could start life anew, he had named Captain Coram one of the trustees of the new colony.

Coram still kept his contact with the American Colonies, and as though even those wide-ranging interests could not suffice as outlets for his energy, he had since interested himself in a plan to provide free passages to Nova Scotia and employment there for unemployed English artisans. This was to serve a double purpose; to help his countrymen, and to secure the new possession against French encroachment.

But how could a conscientious artist hope to limn such a character? The result would depict no more than a large, friendly man dressed in good cloth, without ornament and a little carelessly.

William Hogarth loved to talk, but as an artist he knew the value of getting his sitter to do the talking. Tonight he had the good captain telling of yet another enterprise, as unlike any that had gone before as was possible. Thomas Coram had started a school. Not only a school, but a school in Massachusetts near his shipyard. And not just for the daughters of the settlers, but for the Indian girls.

But why . . . why? What had a bunch of naked savages, females at that, to do with shipbuilding? William choked down his curiosity and produced a mild enquiry. "With what purpose, Coram?"

"It was needed." The deep voice answered with characteristic simplicity. "We have schools in England for boys, but none for girls; and only the daughters of such parents as care to afford tutors for them can even read and cipher. The colonists do things better. Almost all boys, and girls, too, learn to read the Bible at their mother's knee. Many go on to dames' schools. But how can an Indian squaw teach her daughter what she does not know herself?"

Hogarth suppressed a smile. So a busy shipbuilder felt it his duty to add the schooling of Indian girls to his many enterprises!

"A hard night for some of our fellow Londoners," said Captain Coram, noting the sound of sleet still beating against the windows of the warm snug coffeehouse. "The redskins may be savages, but they are better than we are in some ways. We're worse than the Chinese, who expose unwanted girl children to die. We abandon boys as well, hundreds of them every year, in London alone."

Hogarth knew the problem, what Londoner did not? But how to find a remedy? A harlot, or some unfortunate maidservant seduced by her master or a fellow servant, could not support the unwanted child. So she would abandon it on some doorstep, perhaps hoping that it might be taken in. To hang for murder the few luckless women who might be caught in this practice would only add to the fears and miseries of others who would still be forced to the same expedient.

Not even Captain Coram could hope to stop the practice, but it would be interesting to hear his views on it.

Hogarth called for his yard-long clay pipe, and indicated that another should be brought for his friend. Smoking was considered less elegant than the taking of snuff, but it held a man longer to his seat.

"On most evenings I come home on foot from my warehouses at Rotherhithe." The captain applied a taper to his pipe. "Tonight I encountered three such abandoned infants, left in dark alleys, or faintly squalling from under some piles of concealing rubbish. Tonight two were naked, and mercifully dead of the cold. The third, still mewling, lay in a basket upon a doorstep. Perhaps the mother hoped that the people in so comfortable a house would have the charity to take it in, and the means to rear it.

"I rapped upon the door, and told the maid what lay there. She snapped, 'Like enough you left it there yourself! We seen it there an hour back,' and slammed the door in my face. The greatest number are usually to be found along the riverside. Perhaps the mother intends to conceal her crime by throwing the child into the Thames, but at the last moment cannot bring herself to do so. And gives it one more chance; one chance in many thousands perhaps."

Captain Coram's pipe had gone out. He laid it on the table and rose. "Mrs. Coram awaits me. And so unbeautiful a subject as this cannot be of interest to an artist."

Thoughtfully Hogarth watched him stride to the

door; it closed behind the broad shoulders. But what could an artist do, when Captain Coram with all his resources so obviously despaired?

Back home at the Golden Head William could not rid his mind of the problem. Jane recommended a physic for his moodiness, then forced him to tell her his troubles. She contributed further details, including the story of a woman who had exposed no less than ten such unwanted brats, but, her fortunes mending, had reared the eleventh, to become the Master of the Guild of Skinners.

So an unwanted child need not become a defective or criminal man or woman? Yet it was said that ten thousand such were left to die in London alone. The grim picture even began to come between the artist and his work, and it was with relief that, a few evenings later, he found Captain Coram again seated in the Rose.

This time the London sparrow made no attempt to lure the wide-ranging frigate bird into tales of foreign strands and high adventure. Before even ordering his coffee Hogarth plunged straight into the problem of the luckless foundlings.

"You are right," Coram agreed. "Little can be done. But that little must, and can, be done. You shall visit me at Hatton Gardens, and Mrs. Coram will be pleased to show you our adopted family. As the foundlings grow they are no different from what you and I were when young. They are as good, they are as naughty; they are as wise, they are as foolish. And, thanks to Mrs. Coram, just as loving. But we are old to bring up so young a family. And too old to increase it further lest we die and leave their care to strangers. Only a corporation can live on and on."

Hogarth missed the allusion, so Coram had to explain. "For years I and my friends have tried to persuade the Government to establish such institutions as already exist abroad—in Paris, Lisbon, Rome and Madrid. But the same answer comes pat from every minister, and in almost the same words. 'To do so would be to encourage immorality, indeed it would remove its last restraint.' Could cynical indifference mask itself behind fairer words?"

For the first time Thomas Coram sounded bitter, and for the first time in their acquaintance Hogarth was aware of the strong purposeful character behind the man's calm manner and deep pleasing voice. But a man who could bring a dismasted foundering ship safely into harbor, and by skill and dauntless purpose had turned many a threatening failure into success, had been able to do nothing against entrenched indifference.

"Then nothing can be done?"

"What Government refuses to do must be done by others. But even that requires Government consent, for what we need is a charter. That will authorize us to collect money, buy land, and build a hostel for the children; to endow it for their maintenance. We should establish a body of trustees, an undying, corporate body that will do our task long after we are gone. It seems so little a thing to ask, for the charter would cost the Government nothing. I have been sixteen years waiting for this, pleading for this. Sometimes we seem so near to success, but the years go by . . . forgive me for spoiling your evening with what cannot concern you."

But it could and did concern William Hogarth. He took Captain Coram at his word and went to visit the house in Hatton Gardens, and proved, as an expert in reading faces, the fact to his own satisfaction. These children were no different from many others. No one could have guessed that they were waifs and foundlings, picked up from the streets at night, and, wrapped in Captain Coram's ample sea cloak, brought home to this comfortable mansion. Mrs. Coram quite clearly considered them her own to love and care for.

On Hogarth's second visit Jane insisted on accompanying him. But the thought of how narrowly these children had escaped the grim fate of others was too much for her tender heart. Thereafter William went alone. He became a frequent visitor and joined heartily in their games.

Lusty youngsters, they were beginning to burst out of their comfortable nest. And there William introduced them to a new game, so new that no one had ever played it before, he told them.

He stood in the center, as "home base" and numbered them off, half sheepdogs, half shuttles. Then the chant began, led by William.

"The weaver throws his shuttle . . ."

At which half the players danced out from him in straight lines, as a shuttle is thrown.

"The shepherd sends his dog . . ."

And out raced the "dogs" to encircle the "shuttles," but being debarred from breaking the circles in which the sheepdogs tried to round up his flock, found the shuttles most elusive. For the shuttles danced tantalizingly back and forth, nearer to William, as home, then farther off, trying to keep just outside the circle of the pursuing dogs. And the determined "Bow wow wows" of the pursuers shrilly challenged the "clack, clack, clack" of the flaunting shuttles.

But the real bear-garden tumult was waiting for the next lines.

"When the shepherd throws his shuttle
And the weaver sends his dog . . ."

Then shuttles tried to remember to shout "Bow wow wow" and to run in circles, and the dogs to answer "Clack, clack, clack" and race only in straight lines back and forth.

The usual result was a happy chaos, in which William

more than once was thrown to the ground and engulfed in a small determined mob chanting "Clack-wow-clack-bow-clack-wow!"

It was a most popular game, even though it bore hard on William's finery.

Yet, besides these frequent visits, what could he and Jane do to help the children? For the moment they were comfortably well off. But an artist is like a farmer, always dependent upon the success or failure of next season's crops. The Hogarths had no assured incomes, neither had they influential friends at Court who might further Captain Coram's plans. And William's pencil and brush were already at the service of a half dozen causes and sympathies.

For Hogarth this was a busy anxious year. He had held up the issue of the prints of *A Rake's Progress* until his proposed copyright law went into effect. This had been in June of 1735. He was now protected, though a small pamphlet, purporting to be the story of the forthcoming series, was hastily printed by a bookseller and illustrated by some drawings that must have been made from verbal descriptions only. However the sale of the prints was disappointing, far below the striking success of *A Harlot's Progress*. The reason may have lain in the higher price, two guineas for the set of eight instead of a guinea for the set of six. Or, more probably, because it was men who made such purchases, and they found the subject of what might befall their own sex less titillating than the tale of a young girl, innocent and unsuspecting, alone in London.

The studio of the Golden Head was crowded with portraits being painted, proofs arriving from the printer, and plates being engraved. William hired an engraver for the bulk of the work, but always preferred to do the faces himself. There were sketches for new pictures, subscription tickets to be prepared and all the bookkeeping that was involved with this as well. All this pressure of work made him decide to drop out of the group of St. Martin's Lane artists. The school, originally founded by Sir James, had altered its purpose considerably. It had been a most pleasant, informal association and of practical value to its members, but now under the leadership of a young painter newly come to London, Joshua Reynolds, it had developed aspirations, and the group talked of seeking royal patronage and acquiring a Charter of Corporation. Hogarth grumbled disgustedly at the idea. An artist's task was to learn to paint; could a Royal Charter help him do that any better? Indeed, what business was it of the Crown anyway?

More and more subjects came to sit for the now famous William Hogarth. One of these was the kindly gay Lavinia Fenton, grown a little stout and matronly since she had starred in *The Beggar's Opera,* and soon to be married to the Duke of Bolton. Hogarth had painted her in her heyday, as Polly Peachum. His interest in the theatre was scarcely less than his preoccupation with the constant drama of the London streets, and he was already making sketches for *Strolling Actresses Dressing in a Barn*. The subject had special appeal because of a law, newly passed, prohibiting such itinerant players. How could it be right for actors to perform in London, yet wrong for them to do so elsewhere? Such a painting might draw attention to this injustice.

There were countless works in progress, some merely in ideas as yet, some fully sketched, ready to be engraved. Hogarth found time to engrave four earlier pictures, the ones he had painted for Mr. Tyers and the Vauxhall Gardens, *Four Times of the Day*, pictures of his favorite London at various hours and in various moods. For every street, every innyard had its drama, similar to those played out on the stage, and he saw his pictures as stage plays or pantomimes, even arranging the backgrounds with entrances and exits for his characters, these painted very much like stage settings, the foregrounds crammed with stage props.

This love of props, still life for its own sake, increased the more he painted; he used them to explain what was happening to his characters and to tell the reader of the print the social status of his actors, major or minor, and where the act was taking place.

Such details were thickly strewn through *Marriage-à-la-Mode,* which he spent two years in painting. In April 1742 Hogarth ran an advertisement in *The Daily Post,* which read:

Mr. Hogarth intends to publish by subscription, six prints from copperplates, engraved by the best masters of Paris, representing a variety of occurrences in high life, and called Marriage-à-la-Mode. Particular care will be taken, that there may not be the least objection to the decency or elegancy of the whole work, and that none of the characters represented shall be personal.

There had been considerable criticism of his earlier prints; that they dealt only with the low life of London; that they were sordid and disagreeable. At the advice of his friends, in *The Rake's Progress* he had inserted what he felt was a good honest and loyal character, the faithful and rather charming girl whom Tom had jilted. Unfortunately that she should follow him throughout all his debauchery, and even into the madhouse seemed more than improbable, and of course only added to the tragedy.

He was determined to keep the *Marriage* series elegant. Surely it would improve the sales of the prints. But the profit motive of Hogarth the businessman had little control over Hogarth the artist. Once he was caught up in his story he painted it as he saw it.

The first scene, called *The Marriage Settlement* occurs in the fading splendor of the mansion of Lord Squanderfield. The Earl, seated, his gouty foot on a stool, faces a rich merchant and his lawyer, with whom he is discussing the marriage of his son to the merchant's daughter. On the table a document labeled Mortgage, and through the window an addition to the mansion, still half built and in its scaffolding, shows where the money has gone. The merchant on his part holds a document labeled Marriage Settlement. Behind him the two objects of the argument sit back to back; the young viscount, a typical, somewhat effeminate beau, gazes at himself in a mirror while he applies a beauty patch to his cheek. The sullen spoiled little heiress listlessly slides her wedding ring back and forth on her handkerchief, while she listens to the blandishments of the Earl's lawyer, Counsellor Silvertongue.

Here, as usual, Hogarth embellished his scene with explanatory details; the elaborate scroll to which the Earl points a finger, to indicate his noble family tree; the burning candle and sealing wax, to show that the disputed document will eventually be sealed. Often he would return to his copperplate and add another such prop; such items proved their value. They attracted purchasers to the plates, so that even gazing at the print through a shop window the viewer would exclaim, "See the Earl's crutches leaning against his chair. His gout must be very bad, poor fellow," or, "Oh, the merchant is an Alderman. You can tell by the gold chain about his neck. But he's a very common fellow, that shows in the unaccustomed way he wears his sword."

The second picture, *The Viscount and his Lady at Home,* carries the story with only three main characters.

They are shown after a night of gambling and dissipation. The exhausted young viscount sinks into a chair, the lady yawns and stretches beside her tea table, the steward is departing from the room with a handful of papers and an expression of disgust and despair.

But more lies behind this, as the prospective buyer examines the print in all its details. The papers in the steward's hands are unpaid bills; the clock hands point to noon, and though so late in the day the candles still gutter in the chandelier. There has been a party or rout; for on the floor lies a fiddle and a score of music; music, along with quack doctors and absurd wigs were among Hogarth's pet aversions. Not that the viscount attended the rout, he has already begun to lead a separate life as is shown by the broken sword he has thrown on the floor, and the lady's lace cap dangling from his pocket. The smug look of content on his wife's face, her mouth wreathed in a small smile of satisfaction as her eyes glance at him sideways show that she also has her secret amusements. This is marriage-à-la-mode.

With his third scene Hogarth slipped back into the sordid. The viscount has brought a young and imbecile-looking girl and her procuress to the house of a quack doctor, either to have the girl examined or treated. The quack, surrounded by all the paraphernalia of his witch's kitchen, skulls, dried crocodiles, bones and other oddments, is one of the two Hogarth had already painted in the death of Molly Hackabout.

In *The Morning Levee of the Countess*, the artist belatedly recalled his good intentions, and chose a scene with more elegance. Lady, now Countess Squanderfield . . . which is indicated by the coronet above her bed and dressing table, is holding her morning levee, while a Swiss hairdresser attends to her toilette. Counsellor Silvertongue, now her lover, displays some tickets for a masquerade; a musician plays a flute as the great Italian tenor, Farinelli, entertains with a song. A female visitor nearly swoons with delight, and a bored beau, with his hair still in curlpapers, looks on languidly. At their feet a little blackamoor page in a turban unpacks a collection of objets d'art. That the Countess has had a child is shown by the teething coral that hangs on the back of her chair.

In Plate Five the tragic climax of the tale occurs that same evening in a luxurious house of assignation. The Countess has been surprised with her lover, Counsellor Silvertongue. The lawyer and the Earl have fought, and the Counsellor escapes through a window while the young Earl, mortally wounded, appears to fall. Through the doorway comes the landlord accompanied by the night watch.

In his final painting Hogarth could not resist another deathbed scene, or rather death in a chair. The Countess, who has now lost money, husband and lover, has taken poison, and dies in her chair in the center of the stage. Counsellor Silvertongue has been hanged for murder;

this is indicated by a copy of his dying speech and confession which lies at her feet. The nurse holds up her little girl, a cripple with an iron brace on her leg, to kiss the dying mother. The poison is indicated by the physician's reproaching the half-wit servant, and holding the phial to his nose; poverty is shown by a gaunt dog licking a brawn's head on the dirty table, by the cobwebs and a broken chair, and by the father, who draws a valuable ring from the Countess' finger.

Marriage-à-la-Mode did not sell well in the prints. Perhaps again it was too elegant for the common taste of Hogarth's buying public.

THE LONDON OF
PAINTER PUG

9: *Lord Lovat*

LONDON WAS everchanging. The long-extended medieval days had come to an end, and this was now claimed to be the Age of Reason. Once man had entrusted his fate to God, but henceforth he was to be master of his own destiny, guided by no churchly rules save the Light of Pure Reason which flamed within him. If indeed it did.

The outward alterations were more obvious. The picturesque houses which for generations had made London Bridge one of the marvels of England were being torn down to lessen the strain upon the bridge's ancient foundations, and to widen the thoroughfare from the south. No longer would grisly blackened heads adorn Traitors' Gate. And, to the anger of the watermen, there was even talk of building a second bridge across the Thames at Westminster Stairs.

The town houses of the nobility, some almost palaces, which had lined the north bank of the river between London and Westminster were engulfed by a tide of shops and lodgings as the city swept ever westward. Beyond St. Mary le Bon, Clerkenwell and Finsbury Fields, marshes were being drained and farming villages being absorbed to accommodate London's expanding population.

The City government, organized on the basis of craftsmen's guilds, showed little change, and goldsmiths, weavers, tailors, cordwainers, fishmongers, butchers still employed the methods and tools of their fathers and grandfathers. But those guildless outcasts, playactors, artists, poets and writers, began to see a new world opening ahead.

Players were no longer forced to group together in small licensed companies under the patronage and protection of a great noble. It was as though they had ceased to be bound apprentices and had become journeymen craftsmen. They were free to offer their services to this theatre owner or that manager, and to draw their pay of as much as eighteen shillings a week.

Poets still dedicated their verse to wealthy patrons, in expectation of a gift of money, or on rare occasions, of a small life pension. But the growth of a prosperous middle class and a corresponding increase in booksellers enabled other writers to escape from the role of sycophant and sell their literary wares on their own merits.

The range of writing was extending beyond anything ever known in the past. Johnson wrote plays and essays, as well as compiling his noted dictionary. Henry Fielding, a London magistrate, pursued the craft of novelist. Rev. Laurence Sterne, Prebendary of York, was engaged in professional polemics, but was also about to publish the delightful *Tristram Shandy* and migrate to London.

Artists had achieved a nearly professional status—William Hogarth more surely than most. Portraitists must still paint to the approval of sitters, but this is perhaps the curse of the craft; and other painters must cater to the taste, if any, of the well-to-do. Muralists were forced to rely upon commissions from the influential in Church or Government for much of their work. But Hogarth's prints were on sale to all London, and at a price within the reach of any middle-class pocket. He depicted his age and his London, but it was that age and that London which made this possible.

The congestion, lawlessness and filth of the capital seemed to grow worse every year. Not long since, this would have been accepted as God's Will, and hence inevitable. But this was the Age of Reason in which men claimed to be masters of themselves and their environment. They began to ask themselves, what could be done?

Only a rare and unlucky criminal out of hundreds was ever brought to justice, so the severity of legal penalties did little to deter others among the wretched starving throngs from following the same course. A discharged soldier or sailor weighed starvation against the risk of capture, judged it slight, and became a footpad. Even an occasional gentleman, who had gambled away his fortune—and every gentleman gambled—had been known to turn highwayman; while crowding and poverty ensured a continual recruitment of minor criminals, wig-snatchers, cutpurses, pimps and procuresses.

Hogarth had already exposed some of these evils and was later to draw attention to many more. His work did much to arouse the dawning public conscience which is characteristic of this period. But for the moment his whole attention was focused upon one detail of the many-sided problem, the helpless newborn babies for whom their mothers could not provide, and the State refused to. Their only hope, it seemed to him as it had to Captain Coram, lay in the Captain's charitable scheme. If it could ever be put into effect.

Every week, and sometimes more often, William Hogarth stole an hour or two from his busy studio to visit Coram's adoptive family. He taught the children the games, such as grownups played at picnics, evening parties and other frolics; blind-man's buff, ring-around-a-rosy, drop the hankerchief, puss in the corner, and of course London Bridge is falling down, and thoroughly enjoyed the games himself.

But after these visits he returned home in despair, for this very night and tomorrow night and the night after, a dozen or more babies would be exposed to die in London alone, with no kindly Captain Coram to rescue and adopt them. And in late winter such numbers would be doubled and trebled.

In 1739, most unexpectedly, Coram's seventeen years of effort gained their object. A Royal Charter was granted, authorizing the creation of a Foundling Hospital. Now at last there was a Corporation, empowered to raise funds, buy land, build, and organize and govern for charity.

There was only one man fitted to assume the duties of Governor of the Hospital, the man from whose heart and brain it had been born. But the charter had come too late. Captain Coram was now in his seventy-first year. That, he insisted, was too old for the first Governor. His death, which could not be far off, would break the continuity of administration, so necessary for the Hospital in its early days. He would continue to help and advise, but a younger man must take his place, a man thirty years his junior, William Hogarth.

Nothing that Hogarth or others could say would make the old man falter in his unselfish decision. Hogarth, already one of the guardians, assumed his new duties. There was no land, no building, and no money. The first step was to raise funds. To do this there must be fund-raisers, each furnished with a printed authority. Hogarth the Engraver lent his free services to Hogarth the Governor.

Each Power of Attorney had a blank for the name of the collector, and instructions as to how he was to account for the money collected. But this was more than a printed form, for it was headed by an engraving which must have been of considerable value in the appeal for funds. On the left is the doorway of the hospital-to-be, and from it emerges a girl who is greeted by her mother, a boy who carries an astrolabe to indicate that his chosen profession is the sea, and a girl with a spinning wheel to show that she has been taught the skills of a good housewife. These were to show the expected products of the Foundling Hospital. On the right of the engraving a naked baby is shown abandoned beside a stream; in the distance a woman abandoning a similar child, in the center a beadle carrying a newborn child; while beside him is the likeness of Captain Coram (not, it is worth noting, the new Governor William Hogarth) carrying the new charter which will make the kindly miracle possible.

After seventeen years not a day, not an hour could be wasted. Even before the funds were available the search began for a suitable house. None could be found. So land must be bought, though that meant further delay, while the building was designed and built. The Earl of Salisbury, a warm supporter of the charity-to-be, offered fifty-six acres in Lambs Conduit Fields at the bargain price of seven thousand pounds. But the land was far more than the hospital needed and the charity dare offer no more than five thousand of their scanty funds.

The Earl dropped his price by five hundred pounds, but refused to take less or to divide the land. Rather than allow the deal to fall through he offered to subscribe a further five hundred pounds. Necessity, or the foresight of Coram and Hogarth, led them to close with the offer. The large amount of surplus land was ever after to yield a considerable income to the hospital.

At last architectural plans could be drawn up, and the

building started. For the first time a noble dream, a belated charter, could take solid shape in brick and mortar.

William had spent so much time with Captain Coram and the Hospital that he found his income running low. In February, 1745, he held a combined exhibition and auction in his studio. Nineteen paintings were offered for sale. A sale ledger lay open for the whole of the month, one page devoted to the name of each bidder, on which he could write the title of the painting and his offer for it.

Since the studio was small, only those who had inscribed their names and offers in the ledger would be admitted to the final auction, and the sale itself was on the lines of a Dutch or candle auction, but governed by a clock which struck every five minutes. At the end of the first five minutes the first painting was adjudged sold to the man who had written the highest offer in the ledger. Following the second five minutes the second painting was disposed of in the same manner. The six stages of *A Harlot's Progress* sold for fourteen guineas each, the eight stages of *A Rake's Progress* for twenty-two guineas each. *Morning* for eight guineas, *Noon* for thirty-seven guineas, *Evening* for thirty-eight guineas, *Night* for twenty-six guineas, and *Strolling Actresses Dressing in a Barn* for six guineas. It is interesting to note that though the Harlot prints had greatly outsold those of the Rake, the oil paintings of the latter brought half as much again.

Other paintings and drawings were on exhibit, but

not for sale. These included *Marriage-à-la-Mode,* which was still in the hands of the engravers.

Then came the anxious year of the last Jacobite rebellion, affecting even the artist in his crowded studio. In 1745 Prince Charles Edward landed in Scotland to assert his claim to the throne of England. That summer he fought and won the battle of Prestonpans, and before the end of the year he had gathered a large army of Scottish supporters and advanced into England as far as Derby. The fear of these wild Highland invaders seized upon London. City bands were hastily mustered, reinforced by militia regiments and excited mobs, and were marched north to improvise defenses at Finchley.

Hogarth painted *The March to Finchley,* with much intimate detail, including such well-known characters as the inmates of Mother Douglas' brothel and Mother Douglas herself. The painting was both satirical and comic. Somewhat foolishly Hogarth dedicated the prints of it to King George II. But the King was a keen professional soldier. He had done much to organize the army and disliked its being ridiculed by a mere painter. He said as much. Whereat Hogarth turned around and dedicated them to King Frederick of Prussia; also a keen soldier, but in no way averse to seeing the British army made fun of.

Next year the rebellion was driven back to the Highlands. The final battle at Cullodon broke for good the organization of the Scottish clans, and Lord Lovat, their leader, with other rebels was brought south to stand trial for treason.

Simon Fraser, twelfth Baron Lovat, was a crude wily old relic of feudal nobility, a powerful warrior now in his late sixties. He claimed ill health and insisted on being carried all the way south in a litter, to the annoyance of his English captors. The medical attendant assigned to him was a friend of Hogarth's, and knew Hogarth's interest in important criminals, many of which he had drawn and painted in the past.

On August 14 Hogarth set off for St. Albans, and was there received with warm courtesy and Highland charm. Lovat was shaving at the time, and greeted Hogarth in the French fashion with a kiss on both cheeks, leaving a blob of lather on the face of the astonished artist. The Scotsman made no demur at being sketched, and enlivened the tedious business of posing with a frank account of the inside history of the Rebellion.

The result of the sketch, an etching rather than an engraving, was published 'according to Act of Parliament' as the new copyright law required, on August 25. Hogarth had hastened the work as much as possible in order to profit from the public excitement over the State trial, and perhaps also to enlist public sympathy on behalf of this amusing ruffian.

The first impression sold off immediately; the second impression was so much in demand that, priced at a shilling a print, it was bringing in as high as twelve pounds a day, and one bookseller offered Hogarth its weight in gold for the plate; about a hundred and twelve pounds.

If Hogarth's usual warm sympathy for the underdog had led him to hope that he could promote Lord Lovat's cause before his judges, it was in vain. The rebel was adjudged guilty and awarded the usual penalty for high treason. In April of the next year he would be beheaded.

Amid wild scenes such as London had scarce known in living memory; the bogey of invasion by fearsome barbarous Highlanders was now forgotten. Among the handful of nobles who were to suffer the punishment, Lord Lovat at least had captured popular fancy. Throughout his long trial he had shown the primitive courage and scoffing recklessness which promised a stirring final act. Mobs surged through the streets, shops were hastily closed and shuttered, purses were cut, ballads shouted, and on Tower Hill the prisoner's military guard had difficulty in forcing its way through to the headsman and his block.

Good as a highwayman's hanging, it promised to be, for a hanging could be viewed any week of the year, and beheading was a rarity. Some hoped even for the barbarous drawing and quartering, but most knew that a lord could only die by the axe.

Stands had been erected outside the windows and on the ground. Every seat and every inch of standing room was occupied, though the crowd still surged forward. The first of the traitors was already making his last speech, though it had been feared that he might forget it, not knowing the ways as a highwayman would. Impossible to hear a word, but tomorrow the speech would be printed in the penny broadsheets for sale on the streets.

Then came a sound like a cannon shot, on the hill itself. In the startled silence that followed, screams and yells were heard. A stand holding four hundred people had collapsed. Twenty spectators were killed outright, and many more died later of their injuries.

"What's that?" demanded Lord Lovat.

A sheriff told him.

"The more the mischief, the better the sport!" approved that noble and impenitent rascal.

10: David Garrick

"WILLIAM HOGARTH, the painter, I trust?" A young man, as choicely garbed as a beau and as exquisite in his manner, crossed to Hogarth's customary seat in the Rose.

"Also the admirer of David Garrick, the noted playwright and actor." William beamed as they shook hands. This was one great advantage of frequenting a coffeehouse next door to the Drury Lane theatre; one met so many of the actors here.

"So playwright in words meets playwright in pictures! A coffee, sir? Or is chocolate more to your taste?" The young man beckoned a waiter.

William's pleasure increased. Here was a man some twenty years his junior with the perspicacity to discover what few others had noted; that his pictured *Progresses* had indeed been scenes in a play. Eagerly he inquired the cause of Garrick's three years' absence from London. Had he abandoned the boards for his earlier, more lucrative, profession of wine merchant?

Garrick made a graceful gesture with his coffee cup, and quoted a Latin tag. " 'I see the better but follow the

worse.' I am soon to open in good Will Shakespeare's
Richard III, but that is not what brought me to you. I
have a favor to ask." He hesitated, while Hogarth wondered in what way could he serve this talented young
man?

"I have a print of one of your delightful engravings."
Garrick set down his cup and leaned across the bare table.
"It is of *Strolling Actresses Dressing in a Barn*. I count
the print among my most prized possessions. Now I learn
that the original painting is still in your studio. Might I
be allowed to pay my respects at the Golden Head and
view this remarkable work?"

Reluctantly Hogarth had to explain that the late
afternoon light was now too poor to do justice to a work
containing so much detail. But begged that Garrick, his
engagements permitting, would shortly honor him with a
visit.

Actresses dressing in a barn quickly forged a link. It
reminded this exquisite of his second engagement with a
touring company at Ipswich. He had, he said, not actually
been forced to walk behind the wagon that carried the
scenery, but all other comforts and conveniences for the
players were totally lacking. But why had so noted an
artist as Mr. Hogarth interested himself in this side of an
actor's life, so different from his paintings of the stage
scenes of *The Beggar's Opera*?

"It was the iniquity of the new law, which at that time
had prohibited the presentation of plays outside the city

of London," Hogarth explained. "Why should the same play be moral in London and immoral in Ipswich or Bath?"

"And so"—Garrick's magnificent and expressive eyes shone their admiration—"Mr. William Hogarth presented the case of the strolling actresses to the jury of London, and the law was revoked."

What a pleasant young man this was! And how perceptive! William purred like a stroked cat. But then rose reluctantly and excused himself. "I am sorry to depart but I have promised Mrs. Hogarth to accompany her this evening to a friend's. We are newly become the possessors of a carriage and this is her first trial of it. But we shall expect you shortly at the Golden Head, where you will also meet my wife."

The visit occurred only a few days later. Garrick was admitted by a still handsome middle-aged maid in white cap and apron, and having given his name was shown the stairs to the upper floor. At the head of the first flight he encountered the woman's mistress, whom he took to be Mrs. Hogarth, accompanied by two little girls garbed for outdoors. Lacking the formality of an introduction he had to content himself with a slight bow. Mrs. Hogarth must be too accustomed to strangers visiting the studio of her famous husband to wish to make their acquaintance.

The original painting of *Strolling Actresses Dressing*

in a Barn from which the print had been made held Garrick spellbound. And who could better depict a man in the act of being spellbound than this able and courteous young player? What exquisite design! What tasteful color! How packed with story was this small canvas!

Then David Garrick gave a burst of natural laughter. "How well I know them all! If that isn't Carlotts rehearsing her part of Diana in *The Wronged Husband!* What difficulty the manager had with her in keeping that woman sufficiently clothed! And the stacked scenery even tells us what plays are about to be presented! The clothes drying on the line, the rollers to be put under the painted canvas to depict a storm at sea, stockings being darned, sides being rehearsed . . . I could write a play from your props alone.

"And, oh, the expedients we were forced to resort to . . ." He drew a mock sigh. "There is Flora powdering her hair with the flour dredger. She was lucky to have the flour; we had none!" Then his eye fell upon a painted scroll tossed carelessly upon a painted bed; it was to deprive them of their art and livelihood, the Act of Parliament of which he had spoken the other night. He read it, then turned away to other interests in the studio.

There was William's bullfinch Dicky in his wicker cage who must be admired and whistled to in the hope that he would favor the audience with a song. Then back to the paintings again. Garrick of course had seen the two of *The Beggar's Opera* that William had done so long ago. But he had never seen the play itself. Now there was talk of a revival.

Employing his quizzing glass, Garrick examined a print. "An excellent portrayal!" he exclaimed enthusiastically. "One can see the movement, almost hear the tones of the players. But when I have my own theatre I will prohibit spectators in boxes on the stage itself. Their chattering often breaks in on the play, and I have seen actors, who should know better, turn their backs on the audience in the pit to play to some noble patron in a box. Do I not recognize there the Duke of Bolton and his Lavinia?"

"Yes, and since then I have painted two portraits of Lavinia, now the Duchess of Bolton."

Which, in turn, led to Hogarth's exhibiting his painting of the private theatricals, entitled *The Conquest of Mexico*.

"How charmingly you depict young children," said Garrick. "That little girl who is all agog at the play on the stage, and the other who is being pulled back to attention, but cannot help wriggling with boredom. Yes, the children are delightful. You have two of your own? I saw the little girls going out with Mrs. Hogarth as I came up the stairs."

William shook his head. "You know the Cocoa Tree Coffeehouse of course? The little girls, to whom my wife has taken such a fancy, are two of the daughters of the proprietor, Soleiral. He had four, and is hard put to it to give them even a moderate schooling. Mrs. Hogarth has them to tea at times, and now thinks of taking these two into the house for the next few years. We have none of our own."

Garrick was wandering about, gazing at other pictures and engravings. He picked up a print of *The Laughing Audience* which had been done as a subscription ticket to *Southwark Fair,* and *A Rake's Progress.* "I shall also do away, in my own theatre, with those iron spikes between the audience and the orchestra," he declared. "They are both dangerous and unnecessary. If an actor cannot hold his audience in their seats he should not tread the boards."

But Garrick was due at a rehearsal and must regretfully take his leave. The flattered William, after eliciting a promise that the young actor would some day pose for him, followed him down the two flights to the entrance. The same handsome maid opened the door for him and dropped a little curtsey.

A silver coin appeared between Garrick's fingers. But Abigail protested. "Oh, sir, 'twould be more than my place is worth to accept a vail."

"Harsh taskmaster!" said Garrick, turning back to Hogarth. "But since I wish to be remembered by your maid when I call again another vail must avail!" And he gave the flustered Abigail a resounding kiss on her cheek. "Nor can you take this from her."

"We will play that scene again, Mr. Garrick," said Hogarth from the stairs, as though directing from the theatre balcony. "The left foot a little further advanced, and the famous profile presented to this humble audience."

"How careless of me. That can soon be remedied . . ."

"Oh la, sir!" and while Abigail blushed to the roots of her hair, Garrick slowly and lingeringly repeated the short scene, with the corrections Hogarth had suggested.

Strangely enough Hogarth was later the innocent cause of his friend Garrick's discomfiture in the play *Othello*. He was not himself present at the evening's performance, but heard of it at the coffeehouse, where it was the cause of considerable merriment. Garrick played the part in scarlet army tunic, blackened face and high plumed turban, which gave him a chance but unfortunate resemblance to the little blackamoor page, Toby, so well known in *A Harlot's Progress*. Quin the actor, sitting in the audience, caught the striking similarity and in a voice remarkable for its carrying power remarked, "That's Toby. But where's the teakettle?"

The audience was convulsed and Garrick did not play *Othello* again.

It was in December of 1746 that the west wing of the new Foundling Hospital was completed. The hard-working Governor suggested a method by which he and his fellow artists might make the hospital a social as well as a financial success. Newgate Prison, Bridewell and even more, Bedlam the insane asylum, were regularly visited by the fashionable world. The motive might be morbid curiosity, but few sightseers failed to leave a gold piece for the maintenance of the pathetic, half-starved inmates.

Captain Coram's foundation could show no chained and raving lunatics, no dying debtors, no prostitutes being punished for refusing to work; in fact no stench, no squalor, no horrors. What could it offer instead, to start that small but steady flow of gold from curious visitors?

William Hogarth thought he knew the answer. It was as novel as the Hospital itself; no less than an exhibition of art. And what appealed to his north country ancestry was the hope of playing both sides of the same coin. If successful, the scheme would bring generous visitors to donate their alms, put the place in the routine of the world of fashion for future visits, and bring artists in touch with the patrons of art. There might be only two sides to a coin, but William could often find three.

Everything would be clear profit. The name of Joshua Reynolds, already rising to fame as a portraitist, would draw the wealthy connoisseurs. Less esteemed by the critics, but because of his prints the most widely known artist of his day, William Hogarth would attract even more attention. Other painters hastened to contribute their work, for they had nothing to lose and much to gain.

But how would the fashionable world react? In the past, art dealers and noted painters had exhibited in their own limited studios, or carried their wares to the homes of their patrons. There was no tradition of public exhibitions. Also the Foundling Hospital was far off the beaten track of the world of *ton*.

Astonishingly, the first Exhibition was a resounding success. Resentful coachmen and chair porters inquired the way to Conduit Fields. Their masters and mistresses, entranced by the novelty of this break in their routine, bought paintings by artists of whom they might never have heard, and returned home still talking of this strange new venture that seemed to believe it could make good citizens out of babies collected like garbage from the London streets.

So immediate and great was the acclaim that the artists and the Foundling Hospital decided to make the show an annual event. And from that, developed the Royal Academy's annual exhibition and dinner.

It was high time that William Hogarth gave more thought to his own affairs. *Marriage-à-la-Mode,* though it had been specially tailored to fit popular approval, had not sold as paintings and the prints had fared poorly. The scenes of fashionable tragedy had not appealed to the middle-class print buyer, while the fashionable world itself was not amused by this exposure of its own short-comings.

For his next sequence of prints Hogarth found a subject that the Foundling Hospital had brought to his attention. There were good schools, both in London and elsewhere for the sons of yeomen. Hogarth's own father and uncle, though born and bred in a remote country town, could both read and write good English. But such schooling would not be available for the foundlings. They, like the bulk of London children, would be apprenticed to learn a craft. As a one-time apprentice Hogarth well knew the temptations of that training. How then to show this in another sort of progress, a pictured play with a moral and a warning?

So grew the pencil and red chalk drawings for *Industry and Idleness*. He did not paint these, but to save production costs, engraved them himself directly from the sketches.

Out of three thousand crafts and trades that flourished in England, from lamplighters to watchmen, from drapers, barbers, collar makers and so on, Hogarth chose the Huguenot silk weavers of Spitalfields. In these he told the tale of the rewards of virtue and the punishments of vice. Francis Goodchild is at work on his loom while Tom Idle loafs; laziness leads Tom Idle to start on the downward path while playing 'hustle cat' on a gravestone in a graveyard with two ruffians. One step leads inevitably to the next; he is turned off as useless, and is sent away to sea; returns, becomes a highwayman, and so ends on Tyburn Tree. And how encouraging are the rewards of Virtue! The Industrious Apprentice attends church (with the Master's daughter), marries the daughter, becomes Sheriff of the town, and eventually ends as Lord Mayor of London!

The prints had amusing details and secondary plots, but were less complex than the other progresses, and the main story was blunt and obvious. Hogarth intended it so. He hoped that masters would purchase the prints as Christmas gifts to their apprentices, to hang up in the workroom as ever-present reminders. With this in view he sold at the low price of twelve shillings for the set of twelve. Whatever effect they may have had on London's apprentices, the prints were, for the artist, a financial success.

But William had never lost his admiration for Thornhill's Art. Now that money was coming in again and he could afford the time, he dedicated himself to another historical piece; the biblical story of *Paul Before Felix*. It was painted to order, and the large mural-type canvas, which was to hang on the wall of Lincoln's Inn, brought him two hundred pounds.

For this he engraved two separate prints, since in the first one Paul was found to be making a vulgar gesture. Then, purely for his own amusement he scratched a third, a burlesque of the original painting after the manner of Rembrandt. This, for a time, he gave away to friends, but the demand for it became so surprisingly great that he was forced to set a price of five shillings for each additional print; five times as much as for a single one of the *Industry and Idleness* set. Certainly the taste of the public was unpredictable.

11: *A Peregrination to*
a Foreign Shore

IN 1745 William Hogarth painted his own portrait, as a reflection in a mirror gazing out at the spectator. In the lower right-hand corner posed his beloved dog Trump, to whose likeness he devoted as much care as to his own.

Both were honest unassuming portraits, with none of the subtle tricks with which a fashionable portraitist was wont to flatter his sitters. Though forty-eight years old, the smooth rounded face shows little trace of age or of striking character. The ear is well shaped, the nose slightly pug-like rather than patrician, the mouth wide, firm, but remarkably sweet in its expression. The width of the forehead and its unusual central development indicate the excellent visual memory of which he so often boasted.

His studies in physiognomy would have made him aware of what these traits indicated—a pleasant, hardworking middle-class professional, talented, but without genius, who could easily be mistaken for a successful lawyer or merchant. Trump, the dog, is hardly more aristocratic, an amiable, intelligent-seeming pug. The likeness between dog and master caused Hogarth to be labeled with the not unkindly nickname of Painter-Pug; his friends used it in affection, his enemies as a mockery. He was called Hog-pug-ass with monotonous frequency by those same enemies, of which there were not a few.

Some years earlier Hogarth had been a bit of a dandy, but the need or desire for personal advertisement had been removed by success. An unusually happy marriage, an established reputation, a profitable career of his own choosing, and the practical outlet for his kindness and generosity now furnished by the Foundling Hospital gave him such full satisfaction that there was no need to flaunt his ego in dress. The portrait shows him in a montero cap, a sort of turban, as an artist's studio can be chilly for a shaven head, and the loose, comfortable indoor gown which was convenient to work in. The rounded old-fashioned wig and the outmoded roquelaure cloak which he assumed for street wear were no more elegant.

This unpretentious portrait is not complete. Down in the left bottom corner is his palette, on it is shown a double curve, like a slim elongate *S*. It is the symbol of an aspiration, that unattainable ideal which distinguishes the real artist from the hack. Hogarth was writing about it, and later published a book based on this curve, with many detailed engravings, yet he never quite explained the mystic symbol. Perhaps this was impossible. He called it the Line of Beauty.

Saving a noted prize fighter or the Lord Mayor himself, no more familiar figure roamed the streets of London than Hogarth the painter, the engraver of popular prints. Born a Londoner, the streets were still his, as they had been when he rallied to the 'prentices' war cry of "Clubs! Clubs!" The people were his people, virtuous and vicious, and he understood the arts of fraud and robbery as he knew the crafts and the regulations of the Guilds.

For this specialized knowledge he had paid a price of course. Only twice had he set foot outside his home town. Once was on that lighthearted, five-day peregrination to nearby Kent, and that was twenty years ago. On another occasion he had sallied a day's journey north to St. Albans to paint Lord Lovat's portrait. When John Thornhill had suggested that he and Jane move down to Dorset as his guests, the invitation had seemed to William Hogarth a jest in somewhat doubtful taste. One did not leave London!

But now the War of the Spanish Succession came to something like a stalemate, and was ended by the treaty of Aix-la-Chapelle. Britain, the Low Countries, the German States, Sweden, Russia, Austria, France and Italy had all been involved, with subsidiary wars between component parts of the states. At sea, in the West Indies, Britain had been moderately successful, but on land she had suffered defeat before withdrawing the bulk of her forces from the continent to meet the threat of Prince Charles and the Jacobite invasion. This, Hogarth had already recorded in two prints: Lord Lovat and *The March to Finchley*. But a war stretching from Russia to the West Indies had scarcely interested him until it offered him a London street scene under a rebel leader about to be tried in London.

Peace had opened the road from Calais to Paris, and several of Hogarth's artist friends, among them Hayman, Hudson, and Cheere the sculptor, persuaded him to join them in a Continental tour. It was really a business trip, he told himself; he was badly in need of an engraver. In the past he had been partial to Huguenot Frenchmen, so why not visit the studios and ateliers in Paris, where, owing to the recent war, many good craftsmen were known to be unemployed? Also the trip might prove another peregrination, with all its youthful follies and high jinks; everyone is nostalgic for some part of his youth.

Hogarth with his portmanteau took the Dover stage-coach, and with his friends embarked the next morning on the packet boat that had resumed its peacetime sailings. At three that afternoon they dined in Calais. From there they took post-stage to Paris. Hogarth was in a bad mood, and his friends teased him. He was already homesick for his London. Nothing French was to his liking. There were a hundred little pinpricks, different habits and customs, a gibberish language, no good roast beef; it was all ridiculous, and vastly inferior to his London ways and the life that Jane had made so smooth for him.

Also France had suffered from the war, as England had not, so Paris seemed shabby, dirty and unglamorous. The result was that Hogarth vented his disappointment in insulting comments, outright rudeness and bad temper. No attempt to smooth him down had any effect.

Nor did he discover an engraver to his liking in the studios he visited—he was in no mood to—and the Irish and Scots Jacobites who had taken refuge in Paris were able to understand his more than tactless remarks. So Hogarth and Hayman, with some enthusiasm, voted to return home, leaving the others to go on to the Low Countries.

It was in Calais on the way home that Hogarth had the most unfortunate experience of his trip. The packet boat had to await a favorable wind, so while he impatiently prowled the streets he naturally got out his paper and pencil. Over the town gate were carved the coats of arms dating back to the days when the town had been part of England; it was almost a bit of homeland.

His occupation had already aroused interest, for everyone likes to watch an artist at work. But here, in the eyes of the citizens, was something far more serious, a stranger, so recently an enemy, setting down in black and white a picture of the defenses of the town itself!

Hogarth was marched off under immediate arrest. A Londoner, arrested by these shabby French, these frog-eaters, what could be more humiliating? His protests were useless, but perhaps they served some purpose, for he was taken directly to the Governor instead of being clapped into jail for several days.

His protests continued, and to prove his background and his innocence, he showed the Governor the scores of harmless sketches he had made on his visit, Paris streets and people, caricatures of monks, and rough pictorial notes of everyday things and scenes. Surprisingly the Governor, an intelligent man and a connoisseur of art, was interested, even amused. He unbent so far as to admit that nothing he had seen could be of any military value, and that Hogarth was probably not a spy.

"However, m'sieur, were the Peace not already signed it would have been my unamiable duty to have you hanged from the ramparts. But," he gave a ruling, "as it is you will be placed under guard in your lodgings until your packet is on the point of sailing."

Ignominy went even further. In due course Hogarth was marched through the amused crowd to the boat, with a lusty guardsman grasping each arm. The packet was three miles out, about to leave territorial waters, when they spun him round sharply several times, then released him.

"Now, *espion,* you are free to go in whatever direction you wish!" And, chuckling, they dropped into the pilot boat.

It was with enormous relief that Hogarth found himself back in familiar London. But he still fumed at the indignities he had suffered; he, a Londoner! He never had seen much good in France and the French; all through history the Monseers had been England's enemies, and when not fighting they were plotting. They harbored and aided Irish and Scottish malcontents and rebels, and Jesuit spies and plotters. It was they who had landed Charles Stuart the Pretender in Scotland so recently and started the bloody rebellion of '45—though it was Lord Lovat and thousands of good Scotsmen and Englishmen who had died in the attempt—not a single Frenchman! And in less than five years' time there was bound to be another war between France and England.

Let England be warned!

In his studio Hogarth set to work on a painting which should serve both as such a warning and a personal revenge. The painting itself was titled *The Calais Gate* but the subsequent prints were given the more popular title of *O the Roast Beef of Old England!* Hogarth's sharp pictorial criticisms of London suggest the love-hate of a son for a father; but there is no love to temper the bitterness of *The Calais Gate*.

Seen through a shadowed archway as in a frame is the ancient stone gateway, with coats of arms, drawbridge and portcullis. Perched on the summit is a scavenger bird, possibly a raven, symbolic of death and decay. An enfeebled Frenchman staggers under a huge quarter of good English beef, which he carries up from the packet for an English inn. A fat friar, intended to depict the way in which the religious orders battened upon the country, stands close beside, hopefully licking his lips at this rarity. Except for a small figure of Hogarth sketching in the left-hand corner, the other characters are emaciated and in rags, even the two soldiers with fixed bayonets. In the right bottom corner lies, uncared for and seemingly dying, the tartan-clad figure of a Jacobite rebel.

A heavy-handed satire, though no more so than many of the artist's pictures of London, it is clearly as much propaganda as personal spite. Later recruiting posters made use of the figure of one of the French soldiers.

The picture was purchased by Lord Charlemont, and the print advertised for sale in March 1749:

> This day is published, price five shillings, a print designed and engraved by Mr. Hogarth representing a prodigy which lately appeared before the Gate of Calais. O, the Roast Beef of Old England, to be had at the Golden Head in Leicester Fields and at the print shops.

On the continental excursion Hogarth had seen many Jacobite exiles from the rebellion of '45, which reminded him that one of his finest paintings *The March to Finchley*, was still unsold. The Foundling Hospital was now complete so far as building went, but was desperately in need of funds to start the good work. So why not kill two birds with one stone; hold a lottery for the picture and present the proceeds to the Hospital? Or, better still, kill three birds with that stone, by auctioning off prints of *The March* at the same time. In fact, combine all three?

So he offered the prints at a subscription price of seven shillings and sixpence, with the proviso that if any subscriber paid an additional three shillings he would have as well a lottery ticket for the painting.

This ingenious system was a great success. No less than 1843 lottery tickets were sold; 167 were left over. Hogarth presented these to the Foundation, and by a lucky chance the Hospital drew the winning number. Thus they had not only the whole proceeds of the lottery, but the picture itself.

Following Hogarth's example, several other painters presented their work to the Hospital, and so began a collection that became outstanding in London. Handel bequeathed the score of his *Messiah* and for some time continued to give performances in the chapel. Most of the musicians and singers donated their services. Later, Garrick also brought his company to stage plays for the same good cause. The Foundling Hospital was more and more becoming a center of fashion, and of course such publicity was of enormous value to it.

Hogarth presented his fine portrait of Captain Coram to the building, and suggested that it, too, be auctioned off. But later he changed his mind and the portrait remained as a reminder of the generosity of the Founder. Unfortunately, during all these many despairing years, when the good captain had spent all his efforts toward aiding the foundlings, he had also spent all his money on them, and it was finally necessary to procure a pension for him. He died in 1751, two years after he saw his dream fulfilled, and was buried beneath the Hospital. But during his remaining years Captain Coram would have been less than human if he had not found consolation from the fame and prominence of his friend's portrait of him.

It would seem that the organization and supervision, both as Governor and Guardian of the Hospital, would be enough to absorb all of a man's time and energy. But William Hogarth's unwanted babies had a way of growing older, and those first admitted to the West Wing were now aged five and six. Too young to be apprenticed, yet they could not be cast, untrained and inexperienced, into the streets, to earn or beg a living. And every bed in the Hospital was urgently needed for new foundlings. The children must be put with good and honest families. But this must be done with discretion. The farming out of children to women who made a living from it was already one of the scandals of London. Few victims of the system ever survived beyond the first year.

Jane and William not only found money to help support these waifs in good homes, but from time to time took two or more of them to live at the Golden Head.

And yet another problem lay in the future. How would these children fare when exposed to the temptations and the cruelty of London? Hogarth had dealt with some of these problems in his series of *Industry and Idleness*, but since those days another problem had been brought to his attention. This was the increasing drunkenness, and deaths from raw spirits, among the lower classes.

The main cause of this was the cheapness of untaxed Holland gin. "Drunk for a penny, dead drunk for two-pence. Free straw to lie on" was one of the popular slogans. Bootleg distilleries had sprung up everywhere; one house in six was said to dispense the raw spirits. It was even hawked in the streets. Acts of Parliament and other attempts at reform, starting in 1736, had resulted in riots, but in no improvement. "Small" beer, that is beer that is only slightly stronger than flavored water, was the hereditary drink of England as ordinary water was too polluted for safety. Beer could be brewed up to any strength, even of dry wine, but the more potent drinks were too expensive for the ordinary citizen. When distilled spirits first became available to the public they were like a new disease; a plague for which they were not prepared nor immune. Year by year drunkenness among London's population increased, until Henry Fielding, the novelist, taking seriously his duties as a London magistrate, laid a heavy indictment against "Geneva, Hollands, Strong Waters, the Ladies' Delight, King

Theodore of Corsica," and others of similar nicknames for gin.

Immediately following this, Hogarth, a close friend of Fielding's, laid his case before the jury of his fellow Londoners.

The two prints, engraved directly from his pencil and red chalk sketches, were *Gin Lane* and *Beer Alley,* and followed the same direct contrast of good and evil as in those of the two apprentices. *Gin Lane* was an outright horror; a gin addict dying of starvation, another in rags allowing her baby to fall to death down a flight of stairs while behind her the prosperous pawn shop is crammed with people struggling in to sell their last possessions in order to buy more gin. All else in the picture is falling into ruin.

In *Beer Alley* John Bull is shown in his happiest moments. Plump, well-dressed citizens are drinking honest porter; a butcher, a cooper and a drayman comfortably argue, while the cooper waves a leg of mutton to show how easily he can purchase meat and to stress his argument. One of them has thrown his arm around a pretty and neat servant girl; two fishwomen with a flagon of beer have burst into song, and behind them the tavern sign is being freshly painted. Only the pawn shop falls into ruin.

Stimulated by his work on these sketches, Hogarth's hatred of cruelty in any form led him to do a series protesting violently against cruelty to animals. Cock-fighting, bull-baiting, bear-baiting, were the common-place amusements of both gentry and laboring man, but in his pictures he confined his subject matter to the ordinary happenings of the streets.

The *Four Stages of Cruelty* opens with boys inten-tionally and fiendishly torturing cats and dogs. In Stage Two, one of the boys, Tom Nero, has become a hackney coachman. The horse has foundered, overturned the coach and broken a leg; Tom is flogging it with the loaded butt of his whip. While in the background similar scenes take place; a herdsman clubbing a sheep to death, a water carrier driving over the boy who has fallen beneath the wheels of his cart. In Stage Three, Nero has seduced a young girl, persuaded her to rob her mistress and to bring him the silver plate and jewel box. He has just cut her throat to make sure of her silence when he is surprised and seized by her fellow domestics.

In the final Stage, Tom Nero is himself the victim, though dead, with the hangman's rope still encircling his neck. His bare corpse has been handed over for dissection on the slab of Surgeon's Hall. It is a macabre scene, with skeletons hanging from the wall, human skulls and bones being boiled to clean them, while a dog is casually eating what appears to be Tom Nero's heart.

He published these prints at the low price of a shilling each, hoping that he might reach the people he hoped to influence.

As kindly as he was fiery, Hogarth found the horrors of *Gin Lane* and *The Four Stages of Cruelty* an exhausting task, and by way of relief swung back to one of his historical pieces. But *Moses Brought to Pharaoh's Daughter,* though in the style of Thornhill, was not one of his most successful paintings. He gave it to the Foundling Hospital.

12: The Analysis of Beauty

WHAT IS BEAUTY?

As an artist and a teacher of art William Hogarth had long pondered the question and discussed it with his fellow painters. Was there some root principle, some basic test, which would allow just anyone to decide *"This* is beautiful, but *that* is not?"

By 1745 he had boiled down his theory to its quintessence. This, without explanation, he painted in the lower left-hand corner of his self-portrait. A single symbol, a curved line like a very elongated letter *S*, which he labeled The Line of Beauty. It brought both painters and sculptors to his studio to ask its meaning. When he explained, half claimed that they had always used the principle, and half that the principle had never existed.

Out of the collection of papers and notebooks which he had filled with his ideas on the subject of Beauty, he began to evolve what might almost be called Hogarth's Law. A literary friend helped him to sort out his theories and clarify them. By 1751 he had the makings of a book, to be called *The Analysis of Beauty*.

To clarify his ideas he divided them under six headings. *Fitness* required that the parts of a whole, whether a human body or a building, must be functional. *Variety* was needed to relieve the monotony of sameness. *Uniformity* implied symmetry without undue regularity. *Simplicity* should furnish a relief from variety. *Intricacy* should pose a problem which the eye derived pleasure from solving. *Quantity* too had value because sheer size is impressive, whether Windsor Castle or an elephant.

By way of illustration to prove his ideas he engraved two large plates. The first shows a statuary's yard with the sculptures in classical style that were most in fashion. The Laocoon group, Apollo, Venus and Hercules are surrounded by seventeenth-century buildings and accessories. A French dancing master is urging the graceful Antinous to stand up straight and throw his chest out. A statue of a seated judge rests on a capital ornamented, in defiance of Vitruvius and Palladio, with a wig and a tricorn hat. All around this, forming a frieze or frame, run more than fifty minor drawings.

The second plate depicts an assembly in a manor house, in which a dozen or more couples dance gracefully or clumsily beneath a set of royal portraits on the wall. Surrounding this scene is another frame of fifty or so sketches intended for the guidance of students.

The Preface and Introduction open with the modest claim that any lady or gentleman can learn to recognize Beauty, and need not be deterred by the difficulties and the language of Art. But after this mild beginning Hogarth comes out fiercely, graving tool in hand, to give battle in support of his beliefs—and they are many.

Text and detailed illustration give practical instruction to a student. The way to depict age or sex in features and pose. The use of hachuring to indicate distance or shading, whether in engraving, mezzotint or pencil drawing. Under his heading "fitness" he draws attention to occupational characteristics such as the stout legs of a chairman, and the wasted legs but powerful torso of a boatman. On this basis he explains the classical proportions of an Atlas, a Hercules, an Apollo, or a Mercury as suited to the traditional functions they performed.

But before he can concentrate on the "Grammar" of art he must first clear himself of the accusation that he was a lifelong enemy of the Old Masters, Leonardo, Raphael, Tintoretto, and Michael Angelo. This, he protests, is completely false. What arouses his resentment is the fashionable Italianate School, with its slavish copyists, and the fraudulent imitations which were smoked, slashed, rotted, and darkened to give them the appearance of genuine antiques. Not a single work of a single Master now represented the orginal work as it came fresh from the artist's brush. Some colors faded, others darkened, and only ultramarine held its true value; though even this was obscured by coat after coat of darkened varnish. How absurd then for copyists, even honest ones, faithfully to copy these time-corrupted colors and falsify them still further with a coating of brown varnish.

Hogarth's message was clear and forceful. Let English artists follow the example of the Masters themselves, and paint as best they can, with the purest colors and clearest oils that they can find. The Flemish school had already started to do so. His own "historical" paintings show the influence of the classical school and also his admiration for Rubens' use of clear colors.

The Analysis of Beauty is a catch-all for a miscellany of strongly held opinions. Since Man was the highest form of creation, it followed that he was also its most beautiful product; far superior to a greyhound or a race-horse, though these, too, could be beautiful and one more so than another. Another belief was that the female form, having more curves, was therefore more graceful than the male—though here the ancient and admired Greek sculptors would scarcely have agreed.

Such cocksure opinions need to be judged in relation to their period, the eighteenth century, which was the much-vaunted Age of Reason. The philosophers claimed that civilized man had emerged from the Dark Ages in which he was the sport of ignorance and superstition, and was now his own master, in full control of his own destiny. No matter what his problem it could be solved—in theory at least—by the exercise of pure intellect.

That Beauty might "lie in the eye of the beholder"

is too modest and qualified a hypothesis for the day and place, and Hogarth does not even consider it worth mentioning. It exists in nature and in art, therefore it can be sought for, discovered and isolated by anyone who is qualified to recognize it—and Hogarth felt he was. The method is rather like prospecting for minerals.

Since pigments may be beautiful, Hogarth first applies his method of sorting to colors. He arranges them as it were on a palette. Taking red as an example, or sample, he grades it into seven classes. The middle sample is pure red, and is labeled 4. Nos. 5 and 6 are increasingly pale until 7 is pure white. Similarly 3 and 2 grow increasingly dark until 1 is black. "But, as white is nearest to light," he explains," it may be said to be equal if not superior in value as to Beauty with Class 4. Therefore the classes 5, 6 and 7 have almost equal beauty with it, too. Whereas 3, 2 and 1 absolutely lose their beauty by degrees as they approach nearer to black, the representative of darkness."

He does not bring up any arguments in support of this, which suggests that the notion of colors being "beautiful" or not in themselves, and quite apart from their surroundings or individual taste, is an accepted doctrine of his day.

If colors could be divided into classes as more or less beautiful, why could not the same arbitrary rule be applied to form? William Hogarth thought it could. But on this point he does not rely on intuition or his training as an artist, but cites authority.

Thus it was reported that the great Michael Angelo

had instructed his pupil Marcus de Scien "that he should always make a figure pyramidal, serpentlike, and multiplied by the figures 1, 2 and 3." Though this seems somewhat cryptic, Hogarth does not elucidate further. However he clearly takes the "serpentlike" to be his own "line of beauty."

Another expert in the past recommended "Large, flowing, gliding outlines . . . as we see in the Antinous . . . a serpentlike flaming form." Another authority had been more cautious. "Grace and Beauty are two different things; Beauty pleases by the rules, and Grace without them." Unfortunately he does not mention what the rules were.

According to Hogarth's own observation Rubens used a too bold and swelling S-like curve, while Raphael overdid the serpentlike. Peter de Cortone and Corregio followed the same principle. Van Dyke had no idea of it. But Albert Durer was the real heretic, who saw Beauty only in the exact mathematical proportion of each part of the human body.

Not until he was actually at work on the book did Hogarth learn that the search for this germ of Beauty had started even earlier, with Pythagoras. The ancient Greeks had called it Analogy, but had kept the secret from the Romans, with the result that though the Romans had copied from the Greeks they had failed to understand the basic principle.

As a result the Analogy had been lost, and the duty to

recover the rule of Beauty and make it known to the world had fallen upon this middle-aged Cockney. He had no qualms. Whether it was Analogy, Michael Angelo's serpentlike form, or his own Line of Beauty, he knew that he had found the magic symbol.

The pyramidal he also approves, but spends little time on it. Briefly the cone has a certain perfection of shape and outline. The pyramid has this too, and something more besides; for though a cone presents the same appearance from all directions, the pyramid has the advantage of changing outline as the observer walks around. It thus includes the two principles which Hogarth labels Variety and Uniformity.

To establish the Line of Beauty Hogarth engraved in the margin of his first plate seven double curves, the center one, No. 4, being the average and the Line of Beauty. Another figure, of seven curved chair legs, is given elsewhere in the margin, to establish the point that the middle one is the same Line of Beauty. This is a little unfortunate, for the approved curve here is far sharper than the one selected as ideal in the earlier figure. To clinch the argument half of the bottom margin is taken up with seven drawings of women's stays, of which No. 4 again represents the ideal double curve. Unfortunately for proof, it embodies two different curves, one at the back and another at the front, and neither of these agrees with either of the two former ideal curves.

Since such elongated *S*-shapes are rarely found in nature

or in paintings Hogarth imagines them. This is done by picturing a string or wire wound spirally around a thin cylinder, an elongated cone, or part of a human limb. If the string had been real, and the object around which it was supposed to be wound transparent, then the string would be seen as a double-curve. But the demonstration is not convincing.

Whatever we may think of the search for the artists' Holy Grail, the quintessence of Beauty, the book is impressive. William Hogarth had spent two years conscientiously putting on paper what he thought he had learned in his hard-working career. *The Analysis of Beauty* was a generous gift to both art students and art lovers. He was quite unprepared for the effect, which was explosive.

The literary world approved, sometimes warmly, and the work was translated into both French and German, arousing yet more interest. The disapproval of the art world was even more wholehearted. He had attacked the Italianate or Brown Gravy school, and the connoisseurs and art dealers who made their living from it reacted violently. At one time or another Hogarth's prints had ridiculed a host of well-known characters, William Kent, Lord Burlington, Pope, Colonel Chartres, London magistrates, and even notorious procuresses. Many individuals who had felt themselves affronted could now make merry at his expense. Fellow artists, even some friends, resented the air of authority which they felt a mere printmaker had claimed for himself.

Painter Pug—so called from the portrait of himself and his dog—was one of the mildest nicknames now applied to William Hogarth. Almost overnight he became the victim of a campaign of heartless and usually tasteless insult. The London print-sellers did a brisk business in crude and mocking engravings—all the way from a picture of a creature, half pug dog and half human, surrounded by deformed carcasses exemplifying the Line of Beauty, to *The Author Run Mad,* depicting Hogarth, fantastically garbed and crowned, madly daubing away at the walls of his cell. To a sensitive person like William Hogarth it seemed that all his beloved London had turned to rend him.

Bewildered and hurt, Hogarth sought comfort in work. The result was another series, in four prints, called *The Election.* It was a notable departure from his previous work, making use of rural scenes instead of London streets. It also shows little trace of his favorite method of composing a picture after the fashion of a scene on the stage, from the viewpoint of an observer on a level with the principal actors.

The first picture shows the candidate for Parliament feasting his friends and supporters in the parlor of a country inn. Oysters and other luxuries together with much strong drink have already produced their desired effect and a number of undesirable ones. Through the open window can be glimpsed a procession of the rival party with banners and slogans and flying brickbats.

Written signs add further comment on the corrupt politics of the day.

The second picture, *Canvassing for Votes,* gives a charming picture of the outside of a village inn, and the smiling politicians asking and buying votes, while a painting hung beside the inn sign proclaims "Punch, candidate for Guzzletown." In the distance is a mob doing its best to tear down a building, whose owner defends it with a blunderbus. Like the first it is rich with pictorial allusions and innuendos.

In *The Polling,* rival candidates are seated at the back of the booth, while their agents distribute bribes. A paralytic idiot, a criminal in irons, and a bedridden man near death are brought to record their votes, while a soldier lacking a hand and a leg is having his vote protested on the quibble that he cannot lay his right hand on the Bible to take oath.

The final scene is *Chairing the Member.* The successful candidate, fat and terrified, is borne above the heads of his drunken constituents, while a fight breaks out between a countryman with a flail and a sailor with a club.

All four canvases are crowded with figures, stage props and minor stories, as always. They expose abuses, but in so friendly a manner as almost to condone them. They seem aimed at evoking amusement rather than indignation, and lack the harshness and crudity of some of his earlier series. The two years the artist had labored over

his *Analysis of Beauty,* the uproar which had been caused
by its publication, and perhaps the lapse of years begin to
show their effect. William Hogarth was experimenting
along a new line. The four paintings were warmly ac-
claimed, and purchased by David Garrick, now at the
height of his fame.

Now, in 1765, the Continent was at war again. The
Great Powers, France, Russia and Austria were now
aligned against Prussia. Frederick of Prussia called on
Britain for help, and Britain, also isolated, had no choice
but to answer the call. So began the Seven Years War.

In America the French colonial forces had it all their
own way, and within a year England itself faced invasion
by her hereditary enemy. The national morale was at a
low ebb.

Once more Hogarth took to his engraving tools, his
only weapons, and got into the fight. His good friend
David Garrick contributed patriotic verses. The result
was two prints, entitled *The Invasion,* intended to stim-
ulate recruiting. The first one, called *England,* shows a
country boy being measured against a sergeant's halberd,
and standing on tiptoe so as to reach the regulation height.
On a table out of doors beside the Duke of Cumberland
Inn soldiers have laid aside their weapons and with a
sailor are feasting on strong beer and a haunch of beef.
A grenadier is chalking on the inn wall a picture of the
King of France with the ingenuous words blown out of
his mouth "You take a' my fine ships; you be de pirate;

you be de teef; me send all my grand armies and hang you all." Two lusty wenches in the party scream with laughter. In the distance a small group of soldiers are drilling.

The motto, contributed by Garrick runs:

"See John the soldier, Jack the tar,
    With sword and pistol armed for war
    Should mounseer dare come here.
    The hungry slaves have smelt our food
    And long to taste our flesh and blood
    Old England's beef and beer . . ."

ending with a call to arms and prophecy of victory.

The second scene depicts France, preparing the invasion. A ship is waiting in the offing and in the distance soldiers are drilling. For the close-up scene Hogarth has drawn upon his sketches—and prejudices—of *The Calais Gate*. The inn, the Sabot from its sign, is a one-roomed bare affair, with some bare beef bones hung as an attraction in its one unglazed window. Instead of the eager recruit cheating to reach regulation height, a sergeant is forced to goad a soldier on with his halberd. An officer is grilling frogs on his sword, and the only well-fed character is a fat frair assembling instruments of torture for use in an English Holy Inquisition.

Garrick's verse is again neatly in keeping with the crude patriotism:

"With lanthorn jaws and creaking gut
See how the half-starved Frenchmen strut . . ."

and so forth to the fate of the priests . . .

"But, should they sink in coming over
Old Nick may fish twixt France and Dover
And catch a glorious dinner."

Hogarth aimed at popular appeal, not the approval of artistic connoisseurs, and definitely hit his mark. Even so the drawing is less harsh than before *The Analysis of Beauty*. It is worth noting that both scenes were rural. So far as William Hogarth's personal feelings went, London could go hang. But not England.

13: Bathos

HOGARTH WAS deeply hurt by the unexpected and bitter attacks that followed his own attacks upon the Italianate school of painting. But he found comfort in the unshaken belief and support of his friends—such friends as Henry Fielding, the magistrate and novelist; Goldsmith, the young poet; Theophilus Cibber, play producer and manager; David Garrick, and his generous patron for so many years, the Earl of Charlemont.

To avoid the argument and mockery of chance acquaintances he no longer frequented the nearby coffeehouses. London streets had begun to lose their charm, for his strolls could no longer be broken by an occasional halt to admire his own engravings in the shop windows. Prints did indeed continue to be exhibited, and onlookers to be amused by them; but the subject of amusement was more likely to be Hogarth himself. He was now over sixty and began more and more to take himself and his family away to the peace of rural Chiswick and his "villakin" there.

Jane had inherited the place from her mother. It was little more than two hours' ride in the coach, and lay in the cool countryside beside the Thames, near a little hamlet with one street and a single inn. Life there was a complete break from the busy noisy competition of smoky and smelly Leicester Fields. Jane had always loved the place and William now learned to appreciate it.

A brick house, three stories high, square and unpretentious with mansard windowed attics and a chimney at each end, its queer cramped dim rooms and crooked staircases held at times as many as fourteen people. For convenience and more light, rather than for beauty, Hogarth added a large somewhat awkward bow window to the second story, Its main attraction was the ample garden, with gravel walks, a bowling alley, a nut walk, mulberry, cherry and apricot trees, and a hawthorn much favored by nightingales.

Here the hardworking artist began to relax as a family man. And by now it was quite a family. On the death of his sister Mary, Ann had sold out the millinery shop in Long Walk and joined William. Another Mary, Mary Lewis, a young cousin of Jane's, also lived here, and with them there were always two or three children from the Foundling Hospital. Jane's housewifely efficiency was equalled by her quiet tact, and the household, organized around William's life and work and his odd hours in the studio as well as his kindly but irascible temperament, ran happily and without friction.

More furnishings, more servants, were transferred from

the Golden Head, though in the local village Jane found
an excellent nursemaid and attendant to the two little
girls from the Hospital, and an assistant for Cook. This
left a small staff in London to minister to William's needs
when he had to take the family coach back to town.
There were still orders for portraits, he had to see the
publishers about his prints, and was engaged on another
of his biblical paintings.

Sometimes in fine weather they traveled up to the
city by boat or, when he went alone, Jane would send the
coach to fetch him out again. But as a rule she found it
wise to go to London with him, for her Billy was notoriously absent-minded. Once he had been to call on the
Lord Mayor and had arrived back at the Golden Head
drenched from a recent shower.

"Whatever happened to our coach, Billy?" asked Jane,
helping him out of his soaking finery. "Did the man
mistake his orders?"

William looked startled for a moment, then laughed a
little sheepishly. "It must still be waiting for me at the
front door. I was shown out through another door and
completely forgot how I had come there. And with the
shower every hackney I tried to stop was already taken."

With this unpredictability, which would have seriously
disorganized a less flexible household, he arrived unexpectedly one summer evening at the villakin. With
him he brought two guests, also unexpected, David and

Mrs. Garrick, whose portraits he had been painting in town.

London had been hot and fetid, the glare on the river almost as trying. Inside the front gate their feet sank gratefully into the soft green of the lawn, across which trees cast long cool evening shadows. Crab, successor to old Trump, came barking and bounding to greet his master, while the ladies' spaniels followed more demurely. A chattering group of village children were gorging themselves on the ripe purple mulberries; two bullfinches in wicker cages hung from boughs burst into song. Two handsome women of more than middle age and one a little younger put aside their needlework and rose, smiling, to greet the visitors.

Mrs. Garrick, in the French fashion, bestowed a kiss on both of Jane's cheeks and Garrick gallantly bent to kiss the ladies' hands. Then slapping his cocked hat on the rumpled head of the nearest staring urchin he dramatically declaimed "Begone, greasepaint!" Disowning his profession, "Momus, I know thee not!" consigning the critics to oblivion.

The child under Garrick's hat dropped a curtsey. "Please sir, 'tis Molly I am, not Momus."

Jane laughed and went off to call a servant to prepare a room for the guests, and to send a man down to the boat for their baggage.

It was a beautiful midsummer evening, so a cold collation was served in the garden, picnic fashion. On such an evening it would have been cruel to dispatch the two little orphans indoors up to bed, and the village children back to their homes. And somehow it was the children who took possession of the gathering and lent it a rollicking tone of their own.

The incident started when Jane asked David Garrick what play the Drury Lane was now planning to produce.

Garrick gave an airy wave of his hand. "An adaptation of a Shakespeare play called *A Midsummer Night's Dream*. I am calling mine *The Fairies*."

It was the two most staid and solemn members of the company, the foundlings Mary and Susan, who started the frolic. William Hogarth was their well-tried friend, and they had welcomed his return earlier in the evening with squeaks of joy and desperate huggings But youth is fickle and Garrick's charm of voice and manner, which could sway a rough London audience, soon had them in his thrall. At supper they scarce ate a mouthful, but in breathless suspense followed his studied graceful gestures as he talked of the new play.

Now Garrick caught their worshipping glances. As an actor, the greatest of the century, so flattering an audience must not be allowed to escape him, nor be denied the pleasure of seeing him perform. He set down his wineglass and leaped lightly to his feet.

"We will hold a rehearsal of my new play," and he

made a sweeping gesture toward the house behind him. "Imagine this our audience, with pit and balcony. This greensward is our stage, and you my company of players."

Protests and shy hesitation were equally useless. David Garrick was accustomed to having his way. William Hogarth's tentative suggestion that he himself would be a tree trunk around which the fairies danced was dismissed. As Garrick pointed out, "Imagination shall supply the tree, but genius could not supply another Hogarth."

As an inducement to join the cast of players the parson's small son from the village was allowed to wear Garrick's sword, rather to carry it in his hands since Mary Woolaston, the second orphan, insisted on donning the silk sash from which it normally hung. Other garments, cloaks, a bonnet and scarves were hastily fetched from the house, to serve as costumes.

Garrick was often accused of so rewriting Shakespeare's plays that the Bard himself would not have recognized them. But this improvisation on a green lawn of a midsummer's eve ran to sheer madness.

The producer insisted, "But everyone, everyone must play a part," and Garrick hastily improvised lines which they repeated after him, or they made up their own. The dogs were pressed into service as charging knights, or as dragons, though what they were doing in *A Midsummer Night's Dream* no one knew, or specially cared.

"And our good William"—Garrick got to him at last,

for Hogarth, stout and feeling his years, had lapsed into a chair—" since his memory for words is notoriously poor I shall give him a mere two lines. But he must speak those clearly."

Jane ran into the house for paper and pencil to write them down. "I'll fasten it to the back of Ann's fichu and William can stand next to her and read the lines to remind him."

Hogarth bent forward, mumbling the words, and nodding his head wandered away. But five minutes later was back again to reread them. Nor did it seem to matter when or how often in the play that followed he brought them in, nor how malapropos they were; the less they fitted the context the more comic his co-players found them, and the more they laughed.

Of course the main thread of the play, based on Garrick's own performance, was carried by David and his wife. But Ann Hogarth, stout and matronly, with a red scarf rakishly over one eye like a Blackbeard's patch, displayed a surprising talent as captain of a pirate band, gory with mulberry stains and a furled fan for dagger.

At last the children, exhausted with mirth and from shoving the good-natured William from this place and that to t'other on the stage where he was supposed to be, collapsed on the close-scythed lawn. The excited dogs, now doubling as ravening wolves, continued to race round, licking the orphans' faces.

Garrick, regardless of the ripe purple fruit that dotted the lawn, had thrown himself into several assorted parts with his accustomed zeal.

"Oh, if Drury Lane could see you now," said his wife. "You bloodstained monster!"

"Now is the time I should paint your portrait," said Hogarth, taking his revenge." Now you are as I should show you in your portrait. You are in your element when begrimed, and up to your elbows in gore."

The play was ended. Weary and content the village children were dispatched homeward, and the two found-lings sent off to bed. In the peaceful midsummer silence that followed, the moon rose, round and clear, and the nightingale in the hawthorn tree broke into liquid song.

Two days later Hogarth returned to town with the Garricks. He was still dissatisfied with the portrait, and Garrick mounted to the studio to check on its progress, and perhaps put William's doubts to rest.

Hogarth set the canvas on the easel and stood back to survey it. Garrick made a little face and slowly shook his head. "You have caught my wife to the life there, William. It is just so that she plucks a quill from my fingers when she is not agreeable to the part I have written for her in a new play. But . . ." He walked away from it, then went to gaze at himself in a mirror on the wall, and turned back to compare his face with that of the portrait. "But no, it will not do."

Hogarth, reluctantly, agreed. "But who can depict so volatile a countenance. Your expression alters from moment to moment." Then as his peppery temper got the better of him, he picked up a brush, dipped it onto the paint on his palette, and slashed it across the portrait's features.

Garick's shocked expression told Hogarth that the actor had taken the disfiguration of the face almost as a personal assault. "I must do better than that for the famous Garrick," he apologized, "and I shall. When you can again spare the time for a sitting. It is rarely that I catch a likeness on the first attempt."

Garrick smiled his most charming. "Indeed it is seldom that a part comes right at the first reading." And he went away in friendship.

Hogarth put the painting aside for a time. He was very busy with commissions for other portraits, two especially at eighty pounds apiece that had come to him out of his recent appointment as Serjeant-painter to the Crown. John Thornhill, who inherited this sinecure from Sir James, was recently dead. With some pressure from influential friends Hogarth won the appointment, and though it paid only ten pounds a year in quarterly installments, the honor was considerable and the publicity of value. He was also busy painting another historical piece, this time a large altar triptych for St. Mary's.

So versatile and hardworking an artist usually had

several subjects in various stages; sketch, engraving, cartoon for a mural, or the mural itself. Recently some verses had been published in *The Gentleman's Magazine* begging Hogarth by name to expose the barbarity of cockfighting. The idea appealed to him, and such a print could offer a chance to portray many of the notorious "sportsmen" of the day.

That "Royal and Gentle Sport," as popular with the Puritans as with Charles II, was a truly democratic amusement and more popular even than bull-baiting, or beating a blinded chained bear with whips. The skill and valor of the cocks was of only secondary interest. Among all the group shown in this tumultuous and crowded print, only four are following the action of the fight. The avid interest of the misshapen and degraded assembly of thieves, peers, ratcatchers and butchers lies in the betting. Lord Albert Bertie, in Star and Garter decoration, very much the center of the composition, certainly could not prize the sport as he is blind. His hands are in the banknotes he rakes in, one of which is being filched. The French Ambassador, also wearing his decorations, has turned his face away from the fight, in disgust, and exclaims *Sauvages! Sauvages! Sauvages!* One spectator may be the common hangman, for on his back someone had chalked a gibbet, and over the small arena falls the sinister shadow of a man who has failed to pay his wager, and by custom has been hauled up to dangle in a basket. Even from here he reaches out his watch, as a final bet.

Unlike Hogarth's protest embodied in *Strolling Actresses Dressing in a Barn* and to some extent *Gin Lane*, his comment in *The Cockpit* had no effect.

He had now decided to continue with his engraving, but to paint no more. He was weary of portraits, and his large historical pieces had brought him little acclaim, and none of the profit he felt he deserved. But his good friend and constant patron, Lord Charlemont, begged him for one more canvas; the choice of subject and even the price to be set by Hogarth. This was a temptation hard to resist.

The result was *The Lady's Last Stake,* one of his most successful works. In his studio on the top floor of the Golden Head he had sketched in the composition on the canvas and had reached the point when he needed a model. Then Jane came to the door, and with her a young friend of the family, little Lady Hester Salusbury.

She was young, only fourteen, and the lady in the picture would be married. But a model in the studio is worth two in the streets.

"Would you like me to show you what you will look like in ten years' time?" the artist invited. "When you are a grown woman, in silks and satins?"

What young girl would not! And besides William had a charm for children of all ages.

"Then sit here in this chair and let me sketch you.

And if you are patient I will paint you in colors later, so you can see how you are going to look some day." He busied himself with his stick of charcoal, chatting, as any trained artist does, to hold his model's attention.

"The early light is coming through a tall window behind you . . . or behind the lady in the picture. I will show that it is five o'clock in the morning by a clock on the mantelpiece . . . and there is a handsome young officer bending across the table and begging to become your lover. You have been playing at cards all night, and have lost and swept the cards to the floor. The officer holds your losses, your jewels, your money, the miniature of your husband, and half a bank note of five hundred pounds which your husband has sent to you . . ."

"Why only half the bank note, Mr. Hogarth?" Hester wanted to know.

"Because that's the safest way to send money by post," William explained. "People don't steal half-notes, as they are valueless. But when you receive the second half you could then take both to the bank and they would change the note into gold sovereigns."

"It was very wrong of the lady to play cards all the night when her husband was away, now wasn't it?" Hogarth was bringing the story down to the child's understanding. "And very stupid of her to lose all her money and jewels. Now the young officer is trying to take advantage of her. He is offering to stake all that he has won from her against her honor . . . you know what that means of course."

"She would have to undress for him? . . . Even if she didn't love him?"

"Yes, if she lost on her next stake. But she is hoping and wondering if she might win instead, and get back what she has lost before. Isn't she a foolish woman? I am sure we won't call her Hester."

As Hogarth continued to sketch the charming girl, making her a little older for the purpose of the picture, he could not resist reading her a final lecture. "Take you care. I see an ardor for play in your eyes, as in your heart. Don't indulge it." For card playing and gambling was one of the great curses of the day.

The finished picture was a great success with Lord Charlemont. Hogarth presented it without naming a price. His patron, apologetically sent him the sum of a hundred pounds, saying that he was much ashamed to offer such a trifling recompense, so out of keeping with the fame of the artist and the merits of the picture. And Hogarth found even more pleasure in this letter than in the money that accompanied it.

Unfortunately this order led to another similar one, and roused the painter's always dormant ambition to do another historical piece. A painting attributed, probably incorrectly, to the Italian Correggio, had just been sold for four hundred pounds. The subject was Sigismunda,

Boccaccio's tragic heroine, who, more recently had been popularized by Dryden's poem, *Sigismunda and Guiscardo*. The order for a picture came from Sir Richard Grosvenor who, like his friend Lord Charlemont, left both subject and price to the artist.

To show that an Englishman could paint as well as an Italian, Hogarth chose the same subject, thus issuing a direct challenge. The heroine was shown red-eyed and weeping, one hand caressing the head of her dead lover which she has just taken from a casket on the table before her. William painted the doleful face from his memory of a time when Jane had been in tears. But the attempt to portray what Dryden had termed *Mute, solemn sorrow, free from female noise, such as the majesty of grief destroys,* was too ambitious. The picture was a failure.

Hogarth, feeling that he had met the challenge of the Italian master, set the price at four hundred pounds. Sir Richard, seeing the picture while it was still on the easel, refused it on the tactful ground that it was "too melancholy."

Of a sudden the whole world of artists seemed to turn against Hogarth. It mocked, it castigated, it made the picture grounds for vicious personal satire. Even Walpole extolled the Italianate version and condemned the Hogarth one.

The angry and resentful artist decided to lay his case

before a wider jury, the general public. He tried to hire
Ravenet, a skilled French engraver to reproduce it, for if
the prints sold well Hogarth would be vindicated. But
Ravenet's services were already engaged for a full two
years. Hogarth had to return the subscriptions and, to
save face as best he could, presented the painting to Jane
asking that she should never sell it for less than five
hundred pounds.

14: The Last Windmill

HOGARTH's illness which followed seems psychosomatic. His *Analysis of Beauty* had challenged the Italianate school on theoretical grounds. He had been borne down by adverse criticism. *Sigismunda* had attempted to prove, by actual example, that William Hogarth, an Englishman, could rival Correggio (actually Furini) using the same subject and bringing the same price. This time there was no literary approval to soften his defeat by fellow artists and connoisseurs, and he himself had made the challenge so pointed that there was no escaping the verdict. If *Sigismunda* was really the best he could do, then William Hogarth was no painter.

He retired to his villakin to lick his wounds. He was sixty-three years old and growing cantankerous. Also his pride had been hurt in its most tender spot. As a combination of skilled engraver and recorder of his London he had no living rival, but he seems almost to have despised this skill, as a craft, rather than an art. His repeated attempts at the style of Thornhill had varied from acceptable to pretentious failures. His portraits are skillful and downright charming as well as human. His criticism of the worship of antiques and imitation of antiques for age alone and apart from their intrinsic value was wholly justified. But his attempt to humble the Italianate school was nonsensical. Even had his *Sigismunda* been superior to the earlier painting no one would have admitted it. He should have realized as much.

As recently as *The Analysis of Beauty* he had put forward on record his genuine admiration of the Old Masters, and warmly praised the colors of Rubens. But from then on his modesty disappeared.

Few great artists, poets or writers have been good judges of their own work, and if Hogarth undervalued his skill in one direction and overvalued it in another, that was understandable. But during his illness a change occurred. All his life he had yearned to be a great painter. Now his life was nearly ended, he faced the fact that there was no time left in which to demonstrate his mastery. His only comfort was to convince himself, and he seems to have succeeded in doing this.

Kindly, peppery and sensitive all his life, the hurt that he received this time went deeper than before. An embittered old man, the need to assert himself and prove his power became an obsession.

His catalogue of *Pictures exhibited in Spring Gardens* opened with a frontispiece showing British Art being fostered by royal patronage; it ends with a sneer at imported Art, pictured by a Frenchified ape watering some withered "Exotics."

When *Sigismunda* showed no sign of being saleable he put the engraving intended for the lottery tickets on public sale. This engraving was another attack on the Italianate vogue, and showed Father Time with tobacco smoke, a jar of varnish and his scythe "improving" a painting. In another direction he went out of his way to satirize a book on antiquities by a print of the *Five Orders of Periwigs* . . . measured architecturally. Like a hurt dog he snapped at every hand.

Then, reaching back into the past for happier memories, he attempted to draw a portrait profile of the late Henry Fielding. Fielding had died in 1754, and no portrait of him existed.

And back again to a jeering print of a church congregation sunk in *Credulity, Superstition and Fanaticism,* and similar works.

These minor skirmishes gave little satisfaction to his hurt pride, so now he drew out his sharp engraving tools in the cause of national politics. This was a new line for Hogarth, and he would have done better to leave it alone.

George III, young, scrupulously honest and well-intentioned, had come to the throne. As soon as possible he dismissed the corrupt Whig ministry which had ruled the country and took his ex-tutor, Lord Bute, as his main advisor. The Whigs, now in opposition, got to work with a newssheet, *The Monitor,* in which they alleged that Lord Bute was about to betray the country's successful army and navy by a shameful peace with France, and that he was living in adultery with George's sister, the princess. Lord Bute hit back by organizing *The Briton,* a rival newssheet. The Whigs then came out with still another paper, *The North Briton;* Bute responded with yet another, *The Auditor.* Newsprint was as ample as invective.

At this point the luckless Hogarth entered the fight. With Lord Bute, hard-hitting Smollett, Mur and Samuel Johnson on the side of the government, and Lord Temple (Pitt's brother-in-law) served by the brilliant but conscienceless John Wilkes and Charles Churchill on that of the opposition, the choice between right and wrong must indeed have been difficult. Hogarth could not have been very anti-Whig, since around 1760 he engraved a frontispiece and two illustrations for *Tristram Shandy,* dedicated by Sterne to Pitt.

Both Wilkes and Churchill were members of the Shakespeare Club, to which Hogarth and Garrick belonged. Some have guessed that since Hogarth was Serjeant-painter and hence a pensioner of the Crown, a sense of loyalty led him to side with the new government. And against Wilkes and Churchill.

Wilkes was the son of a rich man, and an M. P.,

Churchill the son of an impoverished clergyman, who to gain a living had entered orders. Both were as able and courageous as they were dissolute; Wilkes had a certain nobility of character, Churchill seems to have had no redeeming virtues.

When word passed round that Hogarth was at work on a political engraving, Wilkes sent him kindly advice and warning. Hogarth replied that neither Wilkes nor his friend Churchill would be depicted, but refused to omit Pitt or Lord Temple. Wilkes said that as for himself he did not care, but would take revenge if his two political leaders were attacked.

Hogarth's print *The Times, Plate I* appeared. Basically it represents a house on fire, with Lord Bute and other government figures, trying to extinguish the flames while Pitt, Temple and their supporters obstruct the efforts of the fire fighters and spread the conflagration. Like all Hogarth's work it is full of action and storytelling detail and the political significance of the allusion is of less interest than are the strange methods of fire-fighting in the eighteenth century.

At this time Churchill was laid up with a recurrence of venereal disease, but Wilkes promptly attacked, as he had promised. Heading his piece in *The North Briton* with a caricature of Hogarth he takes a passing shot at *The Analysis of Beauty*, warning the artist to stick to his brush and not take to politics. Then, more cruelly, he hits Hogarth's still-unhealed wound, *Sigismunda*.

Sigismunda, says Wilkes, is not human. If it represents Hogarth's wife 'in an agony of passion,' of what passion no connoisseur could guess. That Hogarth has bored his friends too long with his boasting to have surpassed Raphael, Vandyke and others. Whereas in fact Hogarth is incapable of understanding or portraying happiness or goodwill, because he sees everything as grotesque. Gain and vanity have steered his little bark.

In 1763 Wilkes and fellow editors of *The North Briton* were arrested on a general warrant, but Wilkes was released on grounds of immunity as a member of the House of Commons. Hogarth was present in court, and from the sketches he made there, he did a satiric etching of Wilkes which he sold at a shilling a copy.

Wilkes took it graciously, but his friend Churchill, now recovered, went into action with verse.

"In Comedy . . .
 Hogarth unrival'd stands, and shall engage
 Unrival'd praise to the most distant age . . ."

This tribute paid, he accuses Hogarth of greed, envy, malice, and pictures him as a mental and physical wreck.

"More than half killed by honest truths which fell,
Thro' thy own fault, from men who wished thee well

. . .

. . . Whilst Friends with Friends, all gaping sit, and gaze
To Hear a Hogarth babble Hogarth's praise."

The Whig caricaturists got going, too, ridiculing Hogarth, and of course *The Line of Beauty* and *Sigismunda.*

Horace Walpole disapproved the whole clumsy campaign of vilification, though he, too, had noted Hogarth's increasing habit of extolling himself above the Masters. Garrick, who had tried to intervene on behalf of his friend, was shocked at Churchill's "most bloody performance" and was much concerned for Hogarth's health.

But it was Hogarth's turn again. Either to save time, or to eke out his failing strength, he adapted a copperplate of himself and his dog Trump. Churchill took his place as the main feature, in the guise of a bear with clerical bands, gulping down porter, and holding a knobby club, each knob labeled Lye 1, Lye 2, etc. Trump contemptuously makes water on Churchill's offending verses. Now it was Churchill's turn to feel hurt and indignant.

Satirists threw more fuel on the flames, but without result. The fight was over. Churchill was in serious trouble over a girl, Wilkes was wounded in a duel, disavowed by his masters Pitt and Temple, and to evade a government summons before the House, went into exile in France. Hogarth, whose health and strength were seriously impaired by the strain and emotion of fighting his pointless political and personal battle against the two greatest political writers of the day, was nearing the end.

He lived no more in London, but the engravers came to help him at Cheswick, mainly in revising and retouching existing plates. Here he produced a revised version of the earlier self-portrait; *William Hogarth, 1764.*

Conscious that his time grew short, he announced that he would engrave one final plate, to be called *The End of All Things,* but later changed to *Tail Piece,* and sometimes too aptly called *Bathos.* It reverts to an old theme, and is inscribed *To the Dealers of Dark Pictures.* Time is dying, and breathes the word Finis, while all around him are assembled symbols of destruction, and below two Comic Figures belatedly support the theory of *The Line of Beauty.*

As a last gallant tilt against the windmills it fails to make its point. It is the final despairing statement of the ideals of a lifetime, and more tragic than the engraver could have foreseen. Yet he continued to putter at his work. But as the winter drew in, Hogarth's condition was such that it was thought advisable to move him back to the Golden Head.

Once back in town, his spirits revived, especially on receipt of a letter from Benjamin Franklin. That evening he ate a pound of beefsteak and went to bed in a cheerful mood. But in the night he called for help and died in the arms of his wife's cousin, Mary Lewis.

Hogarth's was a life of contradictions. He may be said almost to have despised the engravings that made him famous, and to have fallen back on them either to urge reform, or as a weapon, or as a livelihood. His near worship of Sir James Thornhill, his friend, teacher and father-in-law, led him constantly to attempt the grandiose paintings for which he had little qualification. His portraits and conversation pieces are often charming, with clear pearly color that has altered little with time. His unfinished sketch of a shrimp girl is a chance masterpiece; we do not know the date of its painting. Like a knight in search of the Grail, he spent his life seeking the underlying principle of all Beauty, and honestly believed that he had found it in a single curve.

Like many another artist he was opinionated and irascible concerning his profession, but largely as a result of the battering he had received over the *Analysis* and *Sigismunda*. It was only then that he attempted to fortify his beliefs by absurd claims to genius, and then only as his powers began to fail.

For a sensitive man, his entry into the political arena against such giants as Wilkes and Churchill was sheer madness, almost the action of a manic depressive. And was virtual suicide.

Behind the artist and harsh satirist lay a person and personality utterly at odds with the public figure. The London cock-sparrow, a man of average size, of hardy, hardworking northern stock, strutting the streets of his beloved city; he took up the very uncertain trade of art, and in his lifetime helped turn painting into an established profession.

He reached the assured and coveted position of favorite pupil and assistant to the noted Sir James Thornhill, and threw it all away to elope with Jane. Then, working harder than ever, regained more than he had lost, and became a prosperous contented husband. Like many artists he was a surprisingly good businessman, though erratic, and at times misjudging the public taste. A single picture was often disposed of as a painting, as a subscription print, and when the plate became worn, as a cheaper print for the general public. Yet, without stint, he gave his services to the Foundling Hospital as well as to several other institutions.

He was peppery and quick-tempered, but with a sweetness and underlying kindness that often removed the sting. The portraits of his six servants show them dignified, contented and mildly amused. Children of all ages adored him. He could, before his quarrel with them, associate smoothly with such men as Wilkes and Churchill; but his personal friends were of rare quality, among the most intelligent of his day, and he could count on such men as Benjamin Franklin among his correspondents. When his father died, his mother and two sisters turned to him for help and advice. So did Lady Thornhill, on the death of Sir James. He gave a permanent home to his sister, and to Jane's younger cousin, and to a succession of orphans. He was a cherished and reliable friend.

Perhaps he was too middle-class, worthy and burdened with responsibilities, to develop the fanaticism of near-genius. Yet it was his striving for the lofty and unattainable that led to *The Analysis* and *Sigismunda,* and thence to the senseless clash that embittered his final days.

Selected Bibliography

Antal, F. *Hogarth's Borrowings*. The Art Bulletin. College Art Association of America. March 1947.

Armstrong, Sir William. *The Art of Hogarth*. Printed as introduction to Austin Dobson's *William Hogarth*.

Bayne-Powell, Rosamond. *Eighteenth Century London Life*.

———.*Housekeeping in the Eighteenth Century*.

Beckett, R. B. *Hogarth*.

Beresford Chancellor, E. *The Annals of Covent Garden and Its Neighbourhood*.

Boas, Frederick S. *An Introduction to Eighteenth-century Drama*.

Bowen, Marjorie. *William Hogarth: The Cockney's Mirror*.

Brown, G. Baldwin. *William Hogarth*.

Burke, Joseph. *The Analysis of Beauty, with Rejected Passages from the Manuscript Drafts and Autobiographical Fragment*. Edited with an Introduction.

Cook, Thomas. *Hogarth Restored*.

Cunningham, Allan. *The Lives of the Most Eminent British Painters*.

Dobson, Austin. *William Hogarth*.

Gaunt, W. *Hogarth*.

George, M. Dorothy. *London Life in the Eighteenth Century*.

Hogarth, William. *The Analysis of Beauty*. MDCCLIII.

Homes Dudden, F. *Henry Fielding, His Life, Work and Times*.

Ireland, S. *Hogarth Illustrated. Graphic Illustrations of Hogarth*.

Mitchell, Charles. *Hogarth's Peregrination*.

Moore, R. E. *Hogarth's Literary Relationships*.

Nichols, J. B. *Biographical Anecdotes of William Hogarth*.

———. *The Genuine Works of William Hogarth: with Biographical Anecdotes*.

Oppé, A. P. *The Drawings of William Hogarth*.

Postgate, Raymond. *That Devil Wilkes*.

Quennell, Peter. *Hogarth's Progress*.

Rocque, John. *Plan of London, 1746*.

Sala, George Augustus. *William Hogarth: Painter, Engraver, and Philosopher*.

Sandby, William. *Thomas and Paul Sandy, Royal Academicians*.

Sitwell, Sacheverell. *Conversation Pieces* and *Narrative Pictures*.

Smith, J. T. *Nollekens and His Times*.

Thrale, H. *Thraliana*, edited by Katherine C. Balderston.

Trusler, The Rev. John. *Hogarth Moralized*.

Walpole, Horace. *Letters. Anecdotes of Painting in England*.

Wheatley, H. B. *London Past and Present*.

———. *Hogarth's London*.

Wilkes, John. *The Correspondence of John Wilkes and Charles Churchill*. Edited with an Introduction by Edward H. Weatherly.

Index

227